MATRIX METHODS

IN

OPTICAL INSTRUMENT DESIGN

WILLEM BROUWER
DIFFRACTION LIMITED
Bedford, Massachusetts

W. A. BENJAMIN, INC.
1964   New York   Amsterdam

MATRIX METHODS IN OPTICAL INSTRUMENT DESIGN

Library of Congress Catalog Card Number 64-21984
Manufactured in the United States of America

*The manuscript was put into production on March 20, 1963;
this volume was published on April 15, 1964*

*The publisher is pleased to acknowledge the assistance of Edith Miller, who
composed the volume; of Russell F. Peterson, who produced the artwork;
and of William Prokos, who designed the cover and dust jacket*

W. A. BENJAMIN, INC.
2465 Broadway, New York, New York 10025

MATRIX METHODS
IN
OPTICAL INSTRUMENT DESIGN

LECTURE NOTES AND SUPPLEMENTS IN PHYSICS

John David Jackson and David Pines, *Editors*

Mathematics for Quantum Mechanics	*John David Jackson (Illinois)*
Elementary Excitations in Solids	*David Pines (Illinois)*
Fundamental Particles	*K. Nishijima (Illinois)*
Matrix Methods in Optical Instrument Design	*Willem Brouwer (Diffraction Limited)*
Relativistic Kinematics	*R. Hagedorn (CERN)*
Quantum Mechanics	*H. A. Bethe (Cornell)*

EDITORS' FOREWORD

Everyone concerned with the teaching of physics at the advanced undergraduate or graduate level is aware of the continuing need for a modernization and reorganization of the basic course material. Despite the existence today of many good textbooks in these areas, there is always an appreciable time-lag in the incorporation of new viewpoints and techniques which result from the most recent developments in physics research. Typically these changes in concepts and material take place first in the personal lecture notes of some of those who teach graduate courses. Eventually, printed notes may appear, and some fraction of such notes evolve into textbooks or monographs. But much of this fresh material remains available only to a very limited audience, to the detriment of all. Our series aims at filling this gap in the literature of physics by presenting occasional volumes with a contemporary approach to the classical topics of physics at the advanced undergraduate and graduate level. Clarity and soundness of treatment will, we hope, mark these volumes, as well as the freshness of the approach.

Another area in which the series hopes to make a contribution is by presenting useful supplementing material of well-defined scope. This may take the form of a survey of relevant mathematical principles, or a collection of reprints of basic papers in a field. Here the aim is to provide the instructor with added flexibility through the use of supplements at relatively low cost.

The scope of both the lecture notes and supplements is somewhat different from the "Frontiers in Physics" series. In spite of wide variations from institution to institution as to what comprises the basic graduate course program, there is a widely accepted group of "bread and butter" courses that deal with the classic topics in physics. These include: Mathematical methods of physics, electromagnetic theory, advanced dynamics, quantum mechanics, statistical mechanics, and frequently nuclear physics and/or solid-state physics. It is chiefly these areas that will be covered by the present series. The listing is perhaps best described as including all advanced undergraduate and graduate courses which are at a level below seminar courses dealing entirely with current research topics.

The publishing format for the series is in keeping with its intentions. Photo-offset printing is used throughout, and the books are paperbound in order to speed publication and reduce costs. It is hoped that books will thereby be within the financial reach of graduate students in this country and abroad.

Finally, because the series represents something of an experiment on the part of the editors and the publisher, suggestions from interested readers as to format, contributors, and contributions will be most welcome.

J. DAVID JACKSON
DAVID PINES

PREFACE

This book consists of my lecture notes of a course given for three years at Boston University. The course was given primarily for Air Force officers. Each year the notes were rewritten to incorporate some of the improvements suggested by the students and other interested individuals. It is hoped that the text will introduce the student to the field of geometrical optics and optical instruments.

These notes might never have been written if I had not had the good fortune to study optics under Prof. Dr. A. C. S. van Heel, whose enthusiasm and capabilities as a teacher showed me the way to this extremely interesting field of physics. I would like to take this opportunity to thank him for guiding me into this field, which has fascinated me ever since and has been a great source of pleasure.

It was the belief in the worth of publishing my course notes and the constant encouragement toward this end of Prof. Dr. E. L. O'Neill that finally brought this book to fruition. It is with further pleasure that I express my appreciation to Dr. O'Neill for taking the time out of his busy schedule to write a portion of Chapter 14.

I am deeply indebted to Harold Merry who made it possible to include so many drawings in the text. His patience with me, his ability to interpret my intentions, and his willingness to redraw till we had what we wanted will be appreciated also by the readers.

My sons, John and Louis, proofread the manuscript and made the index. I am most grateful to them.

The tedious task of editing and guiding the book through the printing was done by Ann J. Quinlan. Without her constant attention and care for details, I do not believe the book would have gotten through this stage.

All the above words of thanks are meant as words of gratitude and not as an excuse for those mistakes which undoubtedly are left and for which I feel personally responsible.

It is my sincere hope that this text will be useful to the many people learning and working in the field of optics.

WILLEM BROUWER

Bedford, Massachusetts
December 1963

CONTENTS

CONTENTS

CONTENTS

Chapter 1

PLANE REFLECTING SURFACES

Rays passing through an optical system, consisting only of plane-reflecting surfaces, undergo a linear transformation. The matrix which describes this transformation should give the transformation of the five coordinates of the incoming ray. In this case, however, we can treat the direction of the ray and the position of a point on the ray separately by asking where a point in space is imaged after passing the reflecting system.

It is clear that we have to solve the problem for one reflection only. If we have a system with more reflections, the matrix of each reflecting surface has to be found, and then these matrices are multiplied in the proper sequence to get the matrix of the whole system.

The mirror is given by the direction cosines ℓ, m, and n of a normal to the mirror and a point P(f, g, h) on its surface with respect to a Cartesian coordinate system. See Fig. 1-1.

We shall first determine the matrix describing the transformation of a point A(x, y, z) by this mirror into point A'(x'y'z'). An easy way to find the matrix is to translate the coordinate system in such a way that its origin is in the point P, then rotate the coordinate system until the z axis coincides with the normal to the mirror. The image of point A in this new coordinate system is easily written since we need only to change the sign of the z coordinate. We now rotate the coordinate system back into its original direction and then translate in such a way as to bring its origin into the original position. The reason for this procedure is that each step can easily be represented by a matrix, and the final result can be found by multiplying the matrices of each step in the correct sequence.

The translation to point P(f, g, h) is given by the matrix

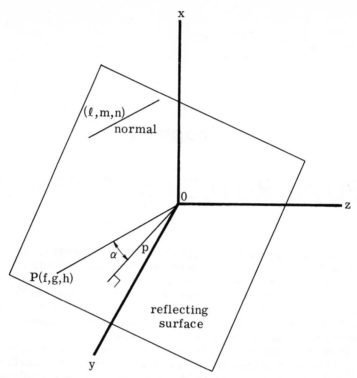

Fig. 1-1.   Coordinate system for plane-reflecting surface.

$$
\begin{bmatrix} x_1 \\ y_1 \\ z_1 \\ 1 \end{bmatrix} = \begin{bmatrix} 1 & 0 & 0 & -f \\ 0 & 1 & 0 & -g \\ 0 & 0 & 1 & -h \\ 0 & 0 & 0 & 1 \end{bmatrix} \begin{bmatrix} x \\ y \\ z \\ 1 \end{bmatrix} = R_1 \begin{bmatrix} x \\ y \\ z \\ 1 \end{bmatrix}
$$

The rotation of the coordinate system until the z axis coincides with the normal on the mirror is undetermined. In our case the position of the x axis and of the y axis is unimportant and can be chosen in a convenient way. Suppose that the new x axis remains in the old xz plane. This is given by

$$R_2 = \begin{bmatrix} n/w & 0 & -\ell/w & 0 \\ -\ell m/w & w & -mn/w & 0 \\ \ell & m & n & 0 \\ 0 & 0 & 0 & 1 \end{bmatrix}$$

in which

$$w = \sqrt{\ell^2 + n^2}$$

It is easily seen that the reflection, derotation, and translation back to the original origin are given by

$$R_3 = \begin{bmatrix} 1 & 0 & 0 & 0 \\ 0 & 1 & 0 & 0 \\ 0 & 0 & -1 & 0 \\ 0 & 0 & 0 & 1 \end{bmatrix} \qquad R_4 = \begin{bmatrix} n/w & -\ell m/w & \ell & 0 \\ 0 & w & m & 0 \\ -\ell/w & -mn/w & n & 0 \\ 0 & 0 & 0 & 1 \end{bmatrix}$$

and

$$R_5 = \begin{bmatrix} 1 & 0 & 0 & f \\ 0 & 1 & 0 & g \\ 0 & 0 & 1 & h \\ 0 & 0 & 0 & 1 \end{bmatrix}$$

The reflection as a whole can now be described by the matrix R where

$$R = R_5 \cdot R_4 \cdot R_3 \cdot R_2 \cdot R_1$$

In doing so we find

$$R = \begin{bmatrix} 1 - 2\ell^2 & -2\ell m & -2\ell n & 2\ell(\ell f + mg + nh) \\ -2\ell m & 1 - 2m^2 & -2mn & 2m(\ell f + mg + nh) \\ -2\ell n & -2mn & 1 - 2n^2 & 2n(\ell f + mg + nh) \\ 0 & 0 & 0 & 1 \end{bmatrix} \qquad (1\text{-}1)$$

The elements of the principal diagonal are equal to the cosines of two times the angles between the coordinate axes and the normal to the mirror.   The geometrical meaning of the term $\ell f + mg + nh$ is easily shown.   The direction cosines of the line 0P are

$$f/0P \quad g/0P \quad h/0P$$

The angle α between this line 0P and the normal on the mirror through 0 is given by

$$\cos \alpha = \frac{\ell f + mg + nh}{0P}$$

and the length p of this normal is

$$p = 0P \cos \alpha = \ell f + mg + nh \tag{1-2}$$

This quantity thus appears to be equal to the distance between the mirror and the origin of the coordinate system.   However, in practice it is often more advantageous to use an intersection of the mirror and one of the coordinate axes as point P.

It is easily verified that the matrix (1-1), read as a determinant, has a value of -1.   This makes it possible to determine directly whether a matrix represents an odd or an even number of reflections in that a determinant of -1 indicates an odd number of reflections and +1 an even number of reflections.

The matrix r, formed by omitting the fourth column and row from the matrix R, represents a mirror containing the origin of the coordinate system.   We notice that terms with quantities of the form $\ell f + mg + nh$ appear only in the fourth column, and thus the matrix r for any given reflecting system consists only of elements formed with the direction cosines of the normals to the mirrors. Thus the matrix r formed in the above manner from the matrix R represents a reflecting system in which all the surfaces are parallel to the given ones with, however, all surfaces passing through the origin of the coordinate system.   Since in such a system the fourth column in the matrix R is composed of all "0's," except the last element which is one, we can reduce this matrix to the 3×3 matrix r.   This matrix represents a rotation of the coordinate system.

The transformation r will image a point P at P' in such a way that the distance 0P equals the distance 0P'.   If the direction cosines of the line 0P are L, M, N and the direction cosines of the line 0P' are L', M', N', we have the following relations:

$$L = x/0P \qquad M = y/0P \qquad N = z/0P$$
$$L' = x'/0P \qquad M' = y'/0P \qquad N' = z'/0P$$

This shows that the matrix r also gives the transformation of the direction cosines, thus

$$\begin{bmatrix} L' \\ M' \\ N' \end{bmatrix} = r \cdot \begin{bmatrix} L \\ M \\ N \end{bmatrix} \qquad (1\text{-}3)$$

Since this is true for each point on a ray, Eq. (1-3) holds also for the direction cosines of an arbitrary ray.

Often in reflecting prisms the light rays pass through them under the same angles of incidence and refraction as in a plane-parallel plate of glass of appropriate thickness. Let L_*, M_*, and N_* represent the normal to the entrance surface and L^*, M^*, and N^* the normal to the exit surface. Then the prism is equivalent to a plane-parallel plate if the image of L_*, M_*, and N_*, indicated by L_*', M_*', and N_*', is parallel to L^*, M^*, and N^*, or

$$L_*'L^* + M_*'M^* + N_*'N^* = 1$$

In matrix notation

$$L^*M^*N^* \cdot r \cdot \begin{bmatrix} L_* \\ M_* \\ N_* \end{bmatrix} = 1 \qquad (1\text{-}4)$$

Let us take as an example a porro prism as shown in Fig. 1-2 with the following values:

$\ell_1 = 0.707$	$m_1 = 0$	$n_1 = 0.707$
$f_1 = 0$	$g_1 = 0$	$h_1 = 1$
$\ell_2 = -0.707$	$m_2 = 0$	$n_2 = 0.707$
$f_2 = -3$	$g_2 = 0$	$h_2 = 0$

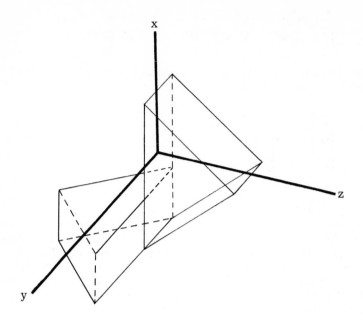

Fig. 1-2.   Porro prism.

$\ell_3 = 0$ $m_3 = -0.707$ $n_3 = -0.707$

$f_3 = 0$ $g_3 = -1$ $h_3 = 0$

$\ell_4 = 0$ $m_4 = 0.707$ $n_4 = -0.707$

$f_4 = 0$ $g_4 = 3$ $h_4 = 0$

From this, with the help of Eq. (1-2), we find

$$p_1 = 0.707 \quad p_2 = 2.121 \quad p_3 = 0.707 \quad p_4 = 2.121$$

Then, with Eq. (1-1), we find

$$\begin{bmatrix} 1 & 0 & 0 & 0 \\ 0 & 0 & 1 & 3 \\ 0 & 1 & 0 & -3 \\ 0 & 0 & 0 & 1 \end{bmatrix} \cdot \begin{bmatrix} 1 & 0 & 0 & 0 \\ 0 & 0 & -1 & -1 \\ 0 & -1 & 0 & -1 \\ 0 & 0 & 0 & 1 \end{bmatrix} \cdot \begin{bmatrix} 0 & 0 & 1 & -3 \\ 0 & 1 & 0 & 0 \\ 1 & 0 & 0 & 3 \\ 0 & 0 & 0 & 1 \end{bmatrix}$$

$$\begin{bmatrix} 0 & 0 & -1 & 1 \\ 0 & 1 & 0 & 0 \\ -1 & 0 & 0 & 1 \\ 0 & 0 & 0 & 1 \end{bmatrix} = \begin{bmatrix} -1 & 0 & 0 & -2 \\ 0 & -1 & 0 & 2 \\ 0 & 0 & 1 & -8 \\ 0 & 0 & 0 & 1 \end{bmatrix}$$

We see that the x and y directions are inverted and the z direction is unchanged. The origin is imaged in the point (-2, 2, -8).

Further information on this chapter can be obtained from Thomas Smith, "On Systems of Plane Reflecting Surfaces," Trans. Op. Soc., **30**, 69-78 (1928-29).

Chapter 2

RAY TRACING

In ray tracing we have two types of transformations of ray coordinates.

    1.   The transformation describing the refraction at a surface.

    2.   The transformation describing the translation of the coordinates to the next surface.

Before going further it is necessary to establish some sign conventions.

    1.   Unless otherwise stated, the light is always coming from the left.

    2.   A distance is positive if measured from left to right.

    3.   A distance is always measured from a refracting surface.

    4.   The vertex of a refracting surface is its intersection point with the axis of symmetry of the system.

    5.   A radius of curvature is positive if the direction from the vertex to the center of curvature is from left to right.

    6.   A ray coordinate before and after refraction will be denoted with the same letter; the one after the refraction will have a prime.

    7.   Indices will be used to indicate at what surface the refraction is taking place. The numbering of the surfaces will be in the order in which the light is passing through them.

Refraction is governed by Snell's law which states that the refracted ray lies in the plane defined by the incident ray and the normal to the point of incidence. Also, in defining the angle of incidence ϕ, as the angle between the incident ray and the normal, and the angle of refraction ϕ', as the angle between the refracted ray and this normal, the relationship between these angles is given by

$$\mu \sin \phi = \mu' \sin \phi' \qquad (2\text{-}1)$$

in which μ and μ' are the refractive indices before and after refraction.

We want to find a formula for the coordinates of the refracted ray in terms of the coordinates of the incident ray. In doing this we will restrict ourselves to spherical surfaces with a radius of curvature r, curvature R = 1/r, and center of curvature C. The systems considered will also have an axis of symmetry, which means that all the centers of curvature of all the surfaces are on one axis.

We now select a coordinate system with the z axis coinciding with all the axes of symmetry and the origin in the vertex of the surface considered, Fig. 2-1. Let AP be an incident ray where P(x, y, z) is the point of incidence of the ray on the refracting surface. The ray is completely defined by giving its direction cosines L, M and the coordinates x, y, z of P. The refracted ray PV can be defined by the coordinates x, y, z of P and its direction cosines L' and M'.

Now extend AP a distance PU, equal to μ which equals the re-

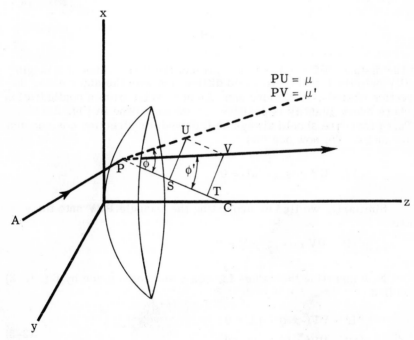

Fig. 2-1. Refraction at a spherical surface.

fractive index to the left of the surface. Next take a distance PV
on the refracted ray equal to μ' which is equal to the refractive index to the right of the surface. PC = r by definition. US and VT
are made perpendicular to PC. Using Snell's law we find

$$US = \mu \sin \phi$$

$$VT = \mu' \sin \phi'$$

$$US = VT$$

(UV is parallel to PC.) We shall need direction cosines (cos α and
cos β) of the line UV which are equal to those of PC. The derivation of the necessary formulas are found in Appendix 2.

With the aid of these formulas we find the direction cosines of
line P(x, y, z) C(0, 0, r) to be

$$\cos \alpha = \frac{0 - x}{r} \qquad \cos \beta = \frac{0 - y}{r}$$

$$= -\frac{x}{r} \qquad\qquad = -\frac{y}{r} \qquad\qquad (2\text{-}2)$$

$$= -xR \qquad\qquad = -yR$$

(The distance PC = r.) We now project the three sides of triangle
PUV onto the x axis. To avoid difficulties with the signs of the direction cosines, it is more convenient to start from a configuration
where every quantity is positive, as we have done in Fig. 2-2.
This procedure should always be followed for direction cosines and
distances. We now see that

$$\mu'L' - UV \cos \alpha - \mu L = 0$$

Similarly, we find by projecting the triangle PUV onto the y
axis

$$\mu'M' - UV \cos \beta - \mu M = 0$$

Now inserting the values for cos α and cos β given by Eq. (2-2)
we find

$$\mu'L' - UV(-xR) - \mu L = 0$$

$$\mu'M' - UV(-yR) - \mu M = 0 \qquad\qquad (2\text{-}3)$$

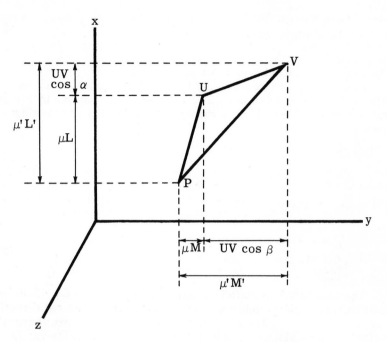

Fig. 2-2. Relation between incoming and refracted ray.

From Fig. 2-1 we see that

$$UV = ST$$
$$= PT - PS \tag{2-4}$$
$$= \mu' \cos \phi' - \mu \cos \phi$$

Let us define a quantity A as

$$A = (\mu' \cos \phi' - \mu \cos \phi)R \tag{2-5}$$

Now

$$UV = A/R$$

and

$$\mu' L' = \mu L - Ax$$
$$\mu' M' = \mu M - Ay$$

$$(2-6)$$

The value of A will change from ray to ray.

At this point it is convenient to introduce the so-called optical direction cosines which are direction cosines multiplied by the refractive index of the medium through which the ray is traveling. Thus

$$\underline{L} = \mu L \qquad \underline{M} = \mu M$$
$$\underline{L}' = \mu' L' \qquad \underline{M}' = \mu' M'$$

$$(2-7)$$

and we now find for Eq. (2-6)

$$\underline{L}' = \underline{L} - Ax$$
$$\underline{M}' = \underline{M} - Ay$$

$$(2-8)$$

The quantity A is called the skew power. From Eq. (2-8) we see that this quantity determines the change in the optical direction cosines of the ray. The greater the value of A the more these direction cosines are changed and thus the direction of the ray is changed. This is why A is called the power.

The addition of the word skew refers to the fact that this power is associated with a particular skew ray, that is, a ray which does not lay in a plane containing the axis of symmetry of the optical system.

Owing to the fact that point P is common to both the incident ray and the refracted ray

$$x' = x \quad \text{and} \quad y' = y \qquad (2-9)$$

Now that we have found the coordinates of the refracted ray in terms of the coordinates of the incident ray we see that the refraction can be described with the following matrices

$$\begin{bmatrix} \underline{L}' \\ x' \end{bmatrix} = \begin{bmatrix} 1 & -A \\ 0 & 1 \end{bmatrix} \begin{bmatrix} \underline{L} \\ x \end{bmatrix} \quad \text{and} \quad \begin{bmatrix} \underline{M}' \\ y' \end{bmatrix} = \begin{bmatrix} 1 & -A \\ 0 & 1 \end{bmatrix} \begin{bmatrix} \underline{M} \\ y \end{bmatrix} \qquad (2-10)$$

In order to follow a ray through an optical system we also need to know the transformation of the ray coordinates from one surface

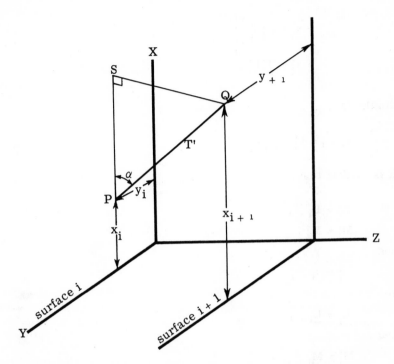

Fig. 2-3. Translation of a ray between two surfaces.

to another. Let us assume that the point of incidence Q on the next surface is known and the distance PQ equals T_i' (Fig. 2-3). We shall refer to the two surfaces as i and i + 1. We now define

$$\underline{T'} = \frac{T_i'}{\mu}$$

Distances divided by the refractive indices are called "reduced" distances. By simple geometry we find

$$
\begin{aligned}
x_{i+1} &= x_i' + PS \\
&= x_i' + T_i' \cos \alpha \\
&= x_i' + T_i' L_i'
\end{aligned}
\tag{2-11}
$$

$$= x_i' + \underline{L}_i' \mu_i' \frac{T_i'}{\mu_i'}$$

$$= x_i' + \underline{T}_i' \underline{L}_i'$$

Similarly

$$y_{i+1} = y_i' + \underline{T}_i' \underline{M}_i' \tag{2-12}$$

It is evident that

$$L_i' = L_{i+1}$$
$$M_i' = M_{i+1}$$

and

$$\mu_i' = \mu_{i+1}$$

so

$$\underline{L}_i' = \underline{L}_{i+1}$$

and

$$\underline{M}_i' = \underline{M}_{i+1}$$

The transformation is now given by

$$\underline{L}_{i+1} = \underline{L}_i'$$
$$x_{i+1} = x_i' + \underline{T}_i' \underline{L}_i' \tag{2-13}$$

and

$$\underline{M}_{i+1} = \underline{M}_i'$$
$$y_{i+1} = y_i' + \underline{T}_i' \underline{M}_i' \tag{2-14}$$

or again, in matrix form

and

$$\begin{bmatrix} \underline{L}_{i+1} \\ x_{i+1} \end{bmatrix} = \begin{bmatrix} 1 & 0 \\ \underline{T}_i' & 1 \end{bmatrix} \begin{bmatrix} \underline{L}_i' \\ x_i' \end{bmatrix}$$

$$\begin{bmatrix} \underline{M}_{i+1} \\ y_{i+1} \end{bmatrix} = \begin{bmatrix} 1 & 0 \\ \underline{T}_i' & 1 \end{bmatrix} \begin{bmatrix} \underline{M}_i' \\ y_i' \end{bmatrix} \tag{2-15}$$

If, in a given optical system for a particular ray, all the values of A and $\underline{T}'$ are known we can form all the necessary matrices. By multiplying these in the correct sequence we find the matrix describing the transformation of the ray coordinates by the whole system. In general this matrix can be written in the following form:

$$\begin{bmatrix} 1 & -A_n \\ 0 & 1 \end{bmatrix} \begin{bmatrix} 1 & 0 \\ \underline{T}'_{n-1} & 1 \end{bmatrix} \begin{bmatrix} 1 & -A_{n-1} \\ 0 & 1 \end{bmatrix}$$

$$\cdots \begin{bmatrix} 1 & 0 \\ \underline{T}'_i & 1 \end{bmatrix} \begin{bmatrix} 1 & -A_i \\ 0 & 1 \end{bmatrix} \begin{bmatrix} 1 & 0 \\ \underline{T}'_{i-1} & 1 \end{bmatrix}$$

$$\cdots \begin{bmatrix} 1 & -A_2 \\ 0 & 1 \end{bmatrix} \begin{bmatrix} 1 & 0 \\ \underline{T}'_1 & 1 \end{bmatrix} \begin{bmatrix} 1 & -A_1 \\ 0 & 1 \end{bmatrix} = \begin{bmatrix} B & -A \\ -D & C \end{bmatrix} \quad (2\text{-}16)$$

(Note that the multiplications must be done in this order.) This matrix is the product of the matrices of the form (2-10) and (2-15), each of which has a value of +1 if computed as a determinant. For this reason the following relationship holds for (2-16):

$$BC - AD = +1$$

This is an important relationship because it gives us a check on the correctness of our matrix multiplication when we work with numerical values for $\underline{T}$ and A.

In order to trace a ray from one medium to another, using the matrix for refraction

$$\begin{bmatrix} 1 & -A \\ 0 & 1 \end{bmatrix}$$

we must first calculate A.

Let us take a simple case. Given a meridional ray in the yz plane and parallel to the z axis (Fig. 2-4) the refractive index to the left of the surface is taken as 1.000 (air) and to the right of the surface as 1.500. We know that

$$A = (\mu' \cos \phi' - \mu \cos \phi)\frac{1}{R}$$

$$= (\mu' \cos \phi' - \mu \cos \phi)0.250$$

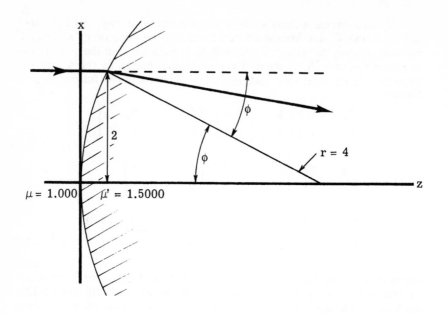

Direction cosines incoming ray	Coordinates of intersection ray and refracting surface
$L = 0$	$x = 2$
$M = 0$	$y = 0$

Fig. 2-4

We see from Fig. 2-4 that

$$\sin \phi = 2/4 = 0.500$$

so

$$\cos \phi = \sqrt{1 - 0.25} = 0.866$$

From Snell's law

$$\mu \sin \phi = \mu' \sin \phi'$$

we get

$$\sin \phi' = \mu/\mu' \sin \phi = 0.5/1.5 = 0.333$$

So

$$\cos \phi' = \sqrt{1 - 1/9} = \sqrt{1 - 0.1111} = 0.943$$

Therefore

$$A = \left(\frac{3}{2} \cdot \frac{2}{3} \sqrt{2} - 1 \cdot \frac{1}{2} \sqrt{3}\right)\frac{1}{4} = \{(1.5)(0.943) - (1)(0.866)\}0.25 = 0.137$$

So our matrix now reads

$$\begin{bmatrix} 1 & -0.137 \\ 0 & 1 \end{bmatrix}$$

In practice we shall always have to go through the process of find-ing $\cos \phi$ by first finding $\sin \phi$, as we have just done.

We shall now give a simple example of the translation of coor-dinates to the next surface (Fig. 2-5).

The coordinates of point P are 2, 0, 0. The ray has direction cosines 0, 0, 1. From the choice of ray it is seen that the x coor-dinate of the point of incidence is 2 and the y coordinate is 0. In order to find T' (the optical thickness for this ray) we must know the z coordinate. In our case this is easily done by using the equa-

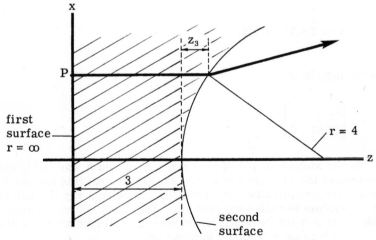

Fig. 2-5. Computations of ray intercept.

tion for a sphere

$$x^2 + y^2 + z^2 - 2rz = 0$$

or, in a more convenient form,

$$z = \frac{x^2 + y^2}{2r - z}$$

By iteration we now find for z

$$z_0 = \frac{4}{8} = 0.5$$

$$z_1 = \frac{4}{8 - 0.5} = 0.533$$

$$z_2 = \frac{4}{8 - 0.533} = 0.536$$

$$z_3 = \frac{4}{8 - 0.536} = 0.536$$

So we now find

$$T' = 3.536$$

and thus

$$\underline{T'} = \frac{2}{3} 3.536 = 2.357$$

and the matrix is

$$\begin{bmatrix} 1 & 0 \\ 2.357 & 1 \end{bmatrix}$$

By the simple choice of the rays considered it was fairly easy to calculate the two types of matrices. In general this becomes much more complicated. Numerically following a ray through an optical system is called ray tracing. This does not necessarily include writing down the matrices involved. Later on we shall discuss the advantages involved in doing so.

The examples do show, however, the essential point. In two places the calculations are not linear. In the case of refraction we

have to convert sines into cosines which is a quadratic operation.
As for the translation, the quadratic form of the surfaces involved
make the calculations quadratic.   This results in the unpleasant
fact that each A and $\underline{T}'$ is different for every ray.   This in turn will
make it difficult for $\overline{us}$ to see what the general properties of the
system are.

More information on this chapter may be found in References
16, 20, 21, 22, 36, and 83.

Chapter 3

PARAXIAL OPTICS

Before going on to investigate the properties of real rays we shall try to get an insight into these properties.

The simplest way to do this is to develop A and $\underline{T}'$ into power series and then consider only the first terms of these series. If only the first terms are considered the results will be approximately true only for small values of the variables. In this case we can expect approximately correct answers only if we consider rays close to the axis of symmetry. Rays traveling further away from this axis might start to deviate markedly from the path predicted by taking only the first terms into consideration. Realizing these restrictions, let us now try to find these approximations.

It is clear that for small values of x, y, L, and M the angles ϕ and ϕ' are very small and thus $\cos \phi \approx \cos \phi' \approx 1$. In this case we denote this approximate value of A by a, which then has the value

$$a = (\mu' - \mu)R \tag{3-1}$$

The first approximation of the value of $\underline{T}'$ will now be the reduced distance between the two surfaces measured along the axis. We will denote this paraxial quantity as $\underline{t}'$, where the understriping again means that this is a reduced distance.

Our matrices now reduce to

$$\begin{bmatrix} 1 & -a \\ 0 & 1 \end{bmatrix} \quad \text{and} \quad \begin{bmatrix} 1 & 0 \\ \underline{t}' & 1 \end{bmatrix}$$

20

We see that the quantities a and t' are constants of the system and any ray is transformed in the same way as long as the above approximation is valid. This gives us a good way to investigate some general properties.

In Fig. 3-1, AB is a ray assumed to be close enough to the

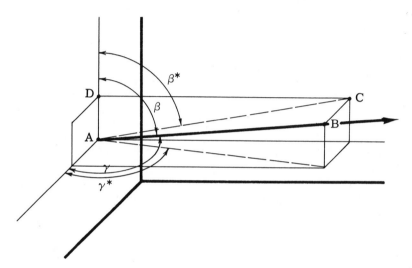

Fig. 3-1. Paraxial ray.

axis to apply to the above approximations. From this figure we have

$$\cos \beta = \frac{AB}{AD} \qquad \cos \beta^* = \frac{AC}{AD}$$

$$AB^2 + BC^2 = AC^2$$

Since AC is a paraxial ray

$$BC \ll AB$$

and thus in our approximation

$$AB^2 = AC^2 \qquad \text{or} \qquad AB = AC$$

and so

$$\cos \beta = \cos \beta^*$$
$$\beta = \beta^*$$

Along the same lines we find

$$\partial = \partial^*$$

In this approximation, therefore, a ray that does not intersect the axis behaves like its projections on the xz plane and yz plane. The transformations these two projections undergo, passing through a system, are the same.

In other words, in this approximation we need consider meridional rays only. A meridional ray is a ray in a plane which contains the axis of symmetry. Assuming our x axis to be in this meridional plane we see that

and
$$L = \cos \beta = \sin \alpha \approx \alpha$$
$$\underline{L} = \mu \cos \beta \approx \mu\alpha = \underline{\alpha}$$
(3-2a)

In the same way

$$\underline{L}' = \mu' \cos \beta' \approx \mu'\alpha' = \underline{\alpha}'$$
(3-2b)

In this approximation (see Fig. 3-2)

$$x \approx h$$
$$x' \approx h'$$
(3-3)

The reason for the minus signs in the matrix is that K. F. Gauss (1777-1855), who formulated these constants for the first time, used a different sign convention. In order to use the same constants, we need to introduce the minus signs in the matrices. The complete transformations now read

$$\begin{bmatrix} \underline{\alpha}'_i \\ h'_i \end{bmatrix} = \begin{bmatrix} 1 & -a \\ 0 & 1 \end{bmatrix} \begin{bmatrix} \underline{\alpha}_i \\ h_i \end{bmatrix}$$

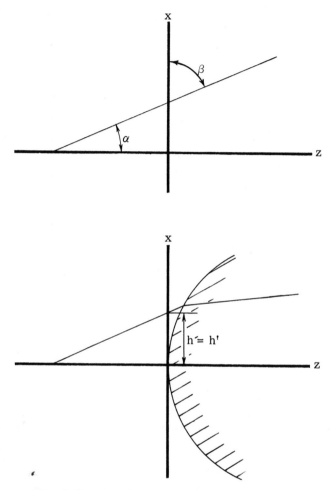

Fig. 3-2. Definition of paraxial variables.

and   (3-4)

$$\begin{bmatrix} \alpha_{i+1} \\ h_{i+1} \end{bmatrix} = \begin{bmatrix} 1 & 0 \\ t' & 1 \end{bmatrix} \begin{bmatrix} \alpha'_i \\ h'_i \end{bmatrix}$$

Now again, for a whole optical system the matrix will have the form

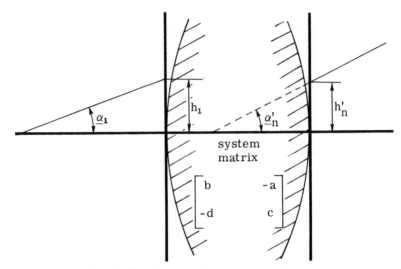

Fig. 3-3. Paraxial system constants.

$$\begin{bmatrix} b & -a \\ -d & c \end{bmatrix} \qquad\qquad (3\text{-}5)$$

and will describe the transformation of a ray entering the system
into one leaving the system. The constants a, b, c, and d are
called the Gaussian constants of the optical system (Fig. 3-3).
The physical significance of these constants as related to the properties of the lens system will be considered in Chap. 4.

An example of the computations of the Gaussian constants appear at the end of this chapter.

The next question that comes to mind is that of image formation. An image is formed when all the light coming from a point P
in the object space goes through one point P' in the image space.
These two points (object and image point) will lay in two planes (object and image plane) perpendicular to the axis of symmetry. The
points can be chosen in the xz plane and will have coordinates
$P(x, 0, z_p)$ and $P'(x', 0, z_p')$. In terms of light rays this means that
all rays going through P before entering the optical system go
through P' after having passed the optical system. This can be expressed mathematically by

$$x' = \beta' x \qquad\qquad (3\text{-}6)$$

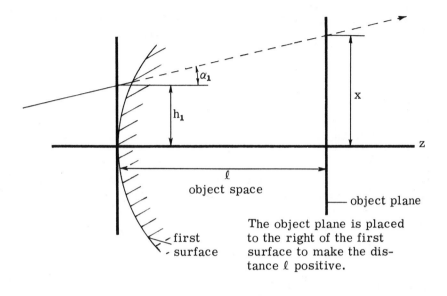

object space

— object plane

The object plane is placed
to the right of the first
surface to make the dis-
tance ℓ positive.

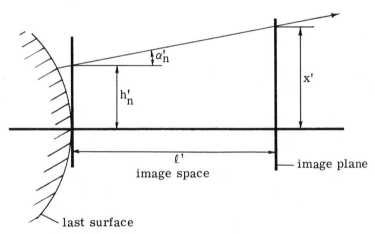

image space

— image plane

Fig. 3-4.   Object and image relationships.

which indicates that x' is independent of the angle α of the rays
(Fig. 3-4).

Let us see if we can find two planes which have this property.
As we have just seen, the transformation of the coordinates of

the rays entering the system at its first surface into the coordinates of these rays emerging from the last surface is given by

$$\begin{bmatrix} \alpha'_n \\ h'_n \end{bmatrix} = \begin{bmatrix} b & -a \\ -d & c \end{bmatrix} \begin{bmatrix} \alpha_1 \\ h_1 \end{bmatrix}$$

or

$$\begin{bmatrix} \alpha'_n \\ h'_n \end{bmatrix} = M \begin{bmatrix} \alpha_1 \\ h_1 \end{bmatrix}$$

However, we want to find the transformation from object-to image-plane, which can be written in the following form:

$$\begin{bmatrix} \alpha' \\ x' \end{bmatrix} = N \begin{bmatrix} \alpha \\ x \end{bmatrix}$$

If we had the following matrices

$$\begin{bmatrix} \alpha_1 \\ h_1 \end{bmatrix} = A \begin{bmatrix} \alpha \\ x \end{bmatrix}$$

which transforms the ray coordinates from the object plane to the first surface of the lens system, and

$$\begin{bmatrix} \alpha' \\ x' \end{bmatrix} = B \begin{bmatrix} \alpha'_n \\ h'_n \end{bmatrix}$$

which transforms the ray coordinates from the last surface of the lens system to the image plane, we could proceed in the following way:

$$\begin{bmatrix} \alpha' \\ x' \end{bmatrix} = B \begin{bmatrix} \alpha'_n \\ h'_n \end{bmatrix} = BM \begin{bmatrix} \alpha_1 \\ h_1 \end{bmatrix} = BMA \begin{bmatrix} \alpha \\ x \end{bmatrix} = N \begin{bmatrix} \alpha \\ x \end{bmatrix}$$

so
$$N = BMA$$

It is easy to find the matrices A and B.

From here on, ℓ will represent a length, that is, the distance from the object plane to the first surface of the lens system, and ℓ'

will represent the distance from the last surface of the lens system to the image plane, and NOT a direction cosine unless otherwise noted.

From Fig. 3-4 we determine

$$h_1 = x - \ell \alpha_1 = x - \underline{\ell} \underline{\alpha_1}$$

with

$$\underline{\ell} = \frac{\ell}{\mu}$$

$$\underline{\alpha} = \alpha_1$$ \hfill (3-7)

or, in matrix form,

$$A = \begin{bmatrix} 1 & 0 \\ -\underline{\ell} & 1 \end{bmatrix}$$

In the same way

$$x' = h'_n + \ell'_n \alpha'_n = h'_n + \underline{\ell}'_n \underline{\alpha}'_n$$

with

$$\underline{\ell}' = \frac{\ell'}{\mu'}$$

$$\underline{\alpha}' = \alpha'_n$$ \hfill (3-8)

or, in matrix form,

$$B = \begin{bmatrix} 1 & 0 \\ \underline{\ell}' & 1 \end{bmatrix}$$

Thus

$$N = \begin{bmatrix} 1 & 0 \\ \underline{\ell}' & 1 \end{bmatrix} \begin{bmatrix} b & -a \\ -d & c \end{bmatrix} \begin{bmatrix} 1 & 0 \\ -\underline{\ell} & 1 \end{bmatrix}$$

$$= \begin{bmatrix} 1 & 0 \\ \underline{\ell}' & 1 \end{bmatrix} \begin{bmatrix} b + \underline{\ell}a & -a \\ -d - \underline{\ell}c & c \end{bmatrix}$$

$$= \begin{bmatrix} b + \underline{\ell}a & -a \\ \underline{\ell\ell}'a + \underline{\ell}'b - \underline{\ell}c - d & c - \underline{\ell}'a \end{bmatrix}$$

For a general choice of the value of $\underline{\ell}$ and $\underline{\ell}'$ we have

$$x' = (\underline{\ell\ell}'a + \underline{\ell}'b - \underline{\ell}c - d)\underline{\alpha} + (c - \underline{\ell}'a)x$$

There is no image formation since this would require x' to be independent of α, as we have seen in Eq. (3-6). If, however, we choose a combination of $\underline{\ell}$ and $\underline{\ell}'$ such that

$$\underline{\ell\ell}'a + \underline{\ell}'b - \underline{\ell}c - d = 0 \qquad\qquad (3-9)$$

we get

$$x' = (c - \underline{\ell}'a)x \qquad\qquad (3-10)$$

which fits perfectly our definition of an image. One can always find a pair of these planes because

$$\underline{\ell}' = \frac{\underline{\ell}c + d}{\underline{\ell}a + b} \qquad\qquad (3-11)$$

and

$$\underline{\ell} = \frac{d - \underline{\ell}'b}{\underline{\ell}'a - c} \qquad\qquad (3-12)$$

So regardless of our choice of $\underline{\ell}$ or $\underline{\ell}'$, the corresponding $\underline{\ell}'$ or $\underline{\ell}$ can always be found. We see also that, once a corresponding $\underline{\ell}$ and $\underline{\ell}'$ are chosen, each point x in this chosen object plane is imaged in a point x' in the image plane, or, the object plane is imaged in the image plane. Every distance p in the object plane is imaged as a distance β'p in the object plane. Comparing Eqs. (3-6) and (3-10) it follows that

$$\beta' = c - \underline{\ell}'a$$
$$\beta' = \text{linear magnification} \qquad\qquad (3-13)$$

Where β' is the linear magnification, we see that the determinant value of the matrices A and B are +1, so that the determinant value of the matrix N which now reads

$$\begin{bmatrix} b + \underline{\ell}a & -a \\ 0 & \beta' \end{bmatrix}$$

(3-14)

should be +1, which gives us

$$N = \begin{bmatrix} \dfrac{1}{\beta'} & -a \\ 0 & \beta' \end{bmatrix}$$

(3-15)

$$\frac{1}{\beta'} = b + \underline{\ell}a$$

(3-16)

Example 1. Given a lens with the physical constants of Fig. 3-5, find the matrix for the system.

$$a_1 = (\mu' - \mu)\frac{1}{r} = 0.5\frac{1}{2.5} = 0.2$$

$$\underline{t'} = \frac{t'}{\mu'} = \frac{0.45}{1.5} = 0.3$$

$$a_2 = (\mu' - \mu)\frac{1}{\infty} = -0.5\frac{1}{\infty} = 0$$

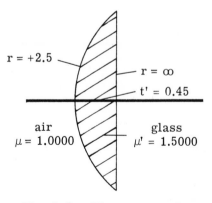

r = +2.5

r = ∞

t' = 0.45

air
$\mu = 1.0000$

glass
$\mu' = 1.5000$

Fig. 3-5. Plano-convex lens.

$$\begin{bmatrix} 1 & 0 \\ 0 & 1 \end{bmatrix} \begin{bmatrix} 1 & 0 \\ 0.3 & 1 \end{bmatrix} \begin{bmatrix} 1 & -0.2 \\ 0 & 1 \end{bmatrix}$$

$$= \begin{bmatrix} 1 & 0 \\ 0 & 1 \end{bmatrix} \begin{bmatrix} 1 & -0.2 \\ 0.3 & 0.94 \end{bmatrix}$$

$$= \begin{bmatrix} 1 & -0.2 \\ 0.3 & 0.94 \end{bmatrix}$$

We check the determinant value of this matrix to determine whether or not the solution is correct:

$$0.94 + 0.06 = 1.0 = \text{the determinant value}$$

PROBLEMS

Problem 1. Given a lens with the physical constants of Fig. 3-6, find the matrix for the system. (The reader must determine

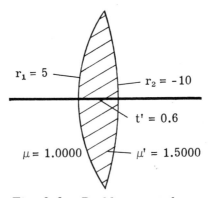

Fig. 3-6. Double convex lens.

the sign of the various quantities.)

Problem 2. Find the matrix of a system composed of the systems of Problem 1 and Example 1 together, using Fig. 3-7.

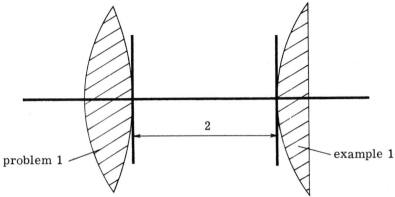

Fig. 3-7.   Lens combination.

ANSWERS

Problem 1:

$$\begin{bmatrix} 1 & -0.050 \\ 0 & 1 \end{bmatrix} \begin{bmatrix} 1 & 0 \\ 0.400 & 1 \end{bmatrix} \begin{bmatrix} 1 & -0.100 \\ 0 & 1 \end{bmatrix}$$

$$= \begin{bmatrix} 0.980 & -0.148 \\ 0.400 & 0.96 \end{bmatrix}$$

Problem 2:

$$\begin{bmatrix} 1 & -0.200 \\ 0.300 & 0.940 \end{bmatrix} \begin{bmatrix} 1 & 0 \\ 2 & 1 \end{bmatrix} \begin{bmatrix} 0.980 & -0.148 \\ 0.400 & 0.960 \end{bmatrix}$$

$$= \begin{bmatrix} 0.508 & -0.281 \\ 2.512 & 0.581 \end{bmatrix}$$

Chapter 4

PARAXIAL PROPERTIES OF LENS SYSTEMS

We have found that

$$\beta' = \frac{x'}{x} \tag{4-1}$$

or, an object of height x is imaged β' times larger. If β' is negative, it means that the image is inverted.

If we take a ray through the axial point of the object $x = 0$, making an angle $\underline{\alpha}$ with the axis, it will go through the axial point of the image, making an angle

$$\underline{\alpha}' = \frac{\alpha}{\beta'} \tag{4-2}$$

[See Equation (3-15).]

Two planes related in such a way that one is the image of the other are called conjugate planes. We can now ask for two conjugate planes which have a magnification of +1. These planes are called unit planes, principal planes, etc. Throughout this book we will label these points with the letter H. All quantities relating to these points will be indicated by a subscript H. To find the position of these unit planes, we make use of formulas (3-13) and (3-16) and find

$$c - \underline{\ell}_H' a = \underline{b} + \underline{\ell}_H a = 1$$

or

$$\underline{\ell}_H' = \frac{c - 1}{a} \quad \text{and} \quad \underline{\ell}_H = \frac{1 - b}{a} \tag{4-3}$$

32

For a ray going through the axial points of the unit surfaces (unit points), it is evident from Eq. (4-2) that the reduced angles with the axis, in the object and image space, are the same.

Until now, object and image distances were measured from the first and last surfaces of the lens system. However, there are advantages in measuring these distances from the unit points.

If we denote these distances by $\underline{s}$ and $\underline{s}'$, we see from Fig. 4-1

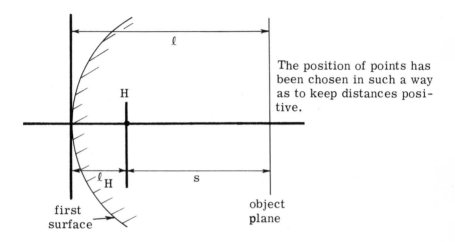

The position of points has been chosen in such a way as to keep distances positive.

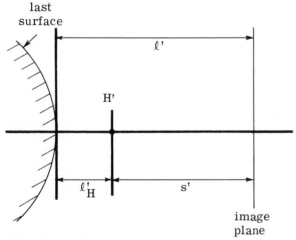

Fig. 4-1.   Object and image planes in relation to the unit points of the lens system.

that

$$\underline{\ell} = \underline{s} + \underline{\ell}_H$$
$$\underline{\ell}' = \underline{s}' + \underline{\ell}_H'$$

$$(4\text{-}4)$$

In order to find the object and image relationship for the new variables, we introduce the above relationships into the matrix N on p. 27. We then find

$$\begin{bmatrix} b + \underline{\ell}a & -a \\ 0 & c - \underline{\ell}'a \end{bmatrix} = \begin{bmatrix} 1 + \underline{s}a & -a \\ 0 & 1 - \underline{s}'a \end{bmatrix} \tag{4-5}$$

and again

$$\beta' = 1 - \underline{s}'a = \frac{1}{1 + \underline{s}a} \tag{4-6}$$

The determinant value of matrix (4-5) is still +1 and thus

$$(1 + \underline{s}a)(1 - \underline{s}'a) = +1$$
$$\frac{1}{\underline{s}'} = \frac{1}{\underline{s}} + a \tag{4-7}$$

This is the well-known equation for paraxial object and image distances.

From Eq. (4-6) we find

$$\frac{\underline{s}'}{\underline{s}} = \frac{\dfrac{1 - \beta'}{a}}{\dfrac{1}{\beta'} - 1}$$

or

$$\frac{\underline{s}'}{\underline{s}} = \beta' \tag{4-8}$$

We can now investigate the meaning of our paraxial constants a, b, and c.

Let us take an object located at infinity. Then

$$\underline{s} = \infty \qquad \text{therefore} \qquad \frac{1}{\underline{s}} = 0$$

and

$$a = \frac{1}{\underline{s'}} = \frac{1}{\underline{f'}} \qquad\qquad (4\text{-}9)$$

Again, if

$$\underline{s'} = \infty \qquad \text{then} \qquad a = \frac{1}{\underline{f}} \qquad\qquad (4\text{-}10)$$

Thus

$$\underline{f'} = -\underline{f} \qquad \text{or} \qquad f' = -\frac{\mu'}{\mu} f \qquad\qquad (4\text{-}11)$$

f' is called the focal length of the system and is directly related to the paraxial quantity a.

The focal length, by definition, is measured from the unit points. Another important quantity is the so-called back focal length ℓ_F', which is the distance from the last surface of the system to the focal point. From Eq. (3-13) we determine

$$c - \underline{\ell'}a = \beta' = \frac{\underline{s'}}{\underline{s}} = \frac{f'}{\infty} = 0$$

so $\qquad\qquad (4\text{-}12)$

$$\underline{\ell}_F' = \frac{c}{a} = c\underline{f'}$$

If we now take $\underline{s'} = \infty$ or $1/\beta' = 0$, we find from Eq. (3-16)

$$b + \underline{\ell}a = \frac{1}{\beta'} = 0$$

so $\qquad\qquad (4\text{-}13)$

$$\underline{\ell}_F = -\frac{b}{a} = b\underline{f}$$

Thus b and c tell us directly what portion of the focal length is outside the lens and indirectly where the unit points are located.

We could also ask ourselves whether or not there are any axial points such that a ray going through these points will make the same angle with the axis of symmetry in the object and image space. For such axial points the condition is

$$\frac{\alpha'}{\alpha} = +1$$

From Eq. (4-2) we determine

$$\underline{\alpha}' = \frac{1}{\beta'} \underline{\alpha}$$

or

$$\frac{\alpha'}{\alpha} = \frac{\mu}{\mu'\beta'}$$

With the above condition

$$\frac{\alpha'}{\alpha} = \frac{\mu}{\mu'\beta'} = 1$$

or   (4-14)

$$\beta' = \frac{\mu}{\mu'}$$

From Eq. (3-13) we determine

$$\underline{\ell}'_N = \frac{c - \left(\frac{\mu}{\mu'}\right)}{a}$$ (4-15)

And from Eq. (3-14)

$$\underline{\ell}_N = \frac{\frac{\mu'}{\mu} - b}{a}$$ (4-16)

These points are called nodal points and will be indicated with the letter N, and quantities related to these points, with the subscript N. We see that for an optical system with the same refractive index for the object and image space, the nodal points and unit points coincide. An example of a case where these points do not coincide is an underwater camera.

The unit points and nodal points as a group are often referred to as cardinal points.

Let us take as an example Fig. 4-2. Then

$$a_1 = (1.5)0.5 = 0.25 \qquad (1.5-1.0).0.5 = (0.5)(0.5) = 0.25$$
$$a_2 = (1 - 1.5)(-1) = 0.5$$
$$\underline{t}' = 0.5/1.5 = 0.333$$

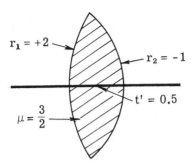

Fig. 4-2. Bi-convex lens.

The matrices of the system are

$$\begin{bmatrix} 1 & -0.500 \\ 0 & 1 \end{bmatrix} \begin{bmatrix} 1 & 0 \\ 0.333 & 1 \end{bmatrix} \begin{bmatrix} 1 & -0.250 \\ 0 & 1 \end{bmatrix}$$

$$= \begin{bmatrix} 1 & -0.5 \\ 0 & 1 \end{bmatrix} \begin{bmatrix} 1 & -0.250 \\ 0.333 & 0.917 \end{bmatrix}$$

$$= \begin{bmatrix} 0.833 & -0.708 \\ 0.333 & 0.917 \end{bmatrix}$$

(This is seen to have a determinant value of +1.) So we now have

$$a = 0.708 \text{ and thus } \underline{f'} = f' = \frac{1}{0.708} = 1.412$$

$$b = 0.833 \text{ and thus } \ell_H = \frac{1 - b}{a} = \frac{1 - 0.833}{0.708} = 0.236$$

$$c = 0.917 \text{ and thus } \ell'_H = \frac{c - 1}{a} = \frac{0.917 - 1}{0.708} = -0.117$$

$$d = -0.333$$

and from this we get

$$\ell'_F = \frac{c}{a} = \frac{0.914}{0.708} = 1.295$$

$$\ell_F = -\frac{b}{a} = -\frac{0.833}{0.708} = -1.176$$

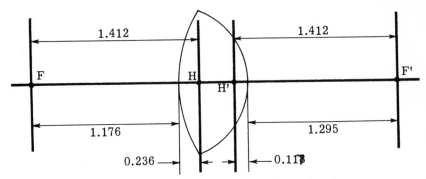

Fig. 4-3. Example of imagery through a lens.

Figure 4-3 illustrates what we have found out about this lens. We now take a ray that strikes the first surface at a height $h_i = 0.353$ and under an angle $\alpha_i = +0.200$. Now we find

$$\alpha_e' = (0.833)(0.2) - (0.708)(0.353) = -0.083$$
$$h_e' = (0.333)(0.2) + (0.917)(0.353) = 0.390$$

This completely describes the ray after leaving the last surface.
    Given the above lens, how are we going to use it in a system to get a magnification of $\beta' = -3$. We know that

$$c - \underline{\ell}'a = -3 \qquad\qquad \underline{\ell}' = \frac{0.917 + 3}{0.708} = 5.532$$

This means that the required image will appear 5.532 units to the right of the second surface of the lens. For $\underline{\ell}$ we find

$$b + \underline{\ell}a = \frac{1}{\beta'} \qquad\qquad \underline{\ell}' = \frac{-0.333 - 0.833}{0.708} = -1.647$$

This is the distance to the left of the first surface of the lens that we must place our object to get the required magnification.
    Let us now take a ray (Fig. 4-4) that leaves the object plane with coordinates

$$\underline{\alpha} = +0.2 \quad\text{and}\quad x = +0.024$$

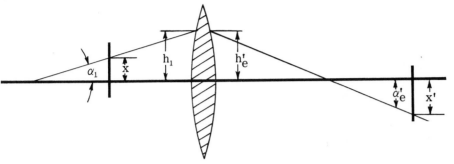

Fig. 4-4. Example with simple lens.

If we now follow this ray step by step through the system, we find for the ray coordinates at the first lens surface

$$h_1 = (1.647)(0.2) + (0.024) = 0.353 \quad \text{and} \quad \alpha_1 = 0.2$$

Now we see that this ray is actually the same one which we traced through this system previously. Using the previous results we know that this ray leaves the lens with coordinates

$$h'_e = 0.390 \quad \text{and} \quad \alpha'_e = 0.083$$

The coordinates of this ray in the image plane are then

$$x' = -(5.532)(0.083) + (0.390) = -0.069$$

and

$$\alpha' = -(0.333)(0.2) - (0.708)(0.024) = -0.084$$

Using system values given earlier, we could have calculated this result directly by use of the proper matrix, thus

$$\begin{bmatrix} \alpha' \\ x' \end{bmatrix} = \begin{bmatrix} \frac{1}{\beta'} & -a \\ 0 & \beta' \end{bmatrix} \begin{bmatrix} \alpha \\ x \end{bmatrix}$$

$$\alpha' = -(0.333)(0.2) - (0.708)(0.024) = -0.084$$

With the aid of Eqs. (4-6) and (4-7), we can calculate $\underline{s}$ and $\underline{s}'$

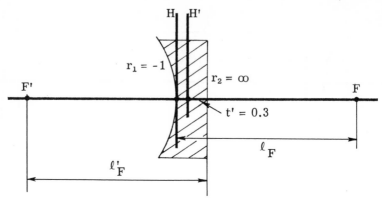

Fig. 4-5.   Plano-concave lens.

directly.

$$\beta' = -3 \quad \text{and} \quad a = 0.708$$

so

$$1 + \underline{s}0.708 = -0.333 \qquad 1 - \underline{s}'0.708 = -3$$
$$\underline{s} = -1.883 \qquad \underline{s} = +5.649$$

Figure 4-5 is an example of a negative lens.

$$a_1 = -0.5 \qquad a_2 = 0 \qquad \underline{t} = 0.2$$

$$\begin{bmatrix} 1 & 0 \\ 0 & 1 \end{bmatrix} \begin{bmatrix} 1 & 0 \\ 0.2 & 1 \end{bmatrix} \begin{bmatrix} 1 & 0.5 \\ 0 & 1 \end{bmatrix}$$

$$= \begin{bmatrix} 1 & 0.5 \\ 0.2 & 1.1 \end{bmatrix}$$

$$\ell_H = \frac{1 - b}{a} = 0$$

$$\ell'_H = \frac{c - 1}{a} = \frac{0.1}{-0.5} = -0.2$$

$$\ell_F = -\frac{b}{a} = -\frac{1}{-0.5} = +0.2$$

$$\ell'_F = \frac{c}{a} = \frac{1.1}{-0.5} = -2.2$$

THE SINGLE LENS

Suppose we know the physical shape of the lens, that is to say, r_1, t, μ, and r_2. We can then calculate a_1, t, and a_2. This lens can now be represented by

$$\begin{bmatrix} 1 & -a_2 \\ 0 & 1 \end{bmatrix} \begin{bmatrix} 1 & 0 \\ \underline{t}' & 1 \end{bmatrix} \begin{bmatrix} 1 & -a_1 \\ 0 & 1 \end{bmatrix}$$

$$= \begin{bmatrix} 1 - \underline{t}'a_2 & -a_1 - a_2 + \underline{t}'a_1 a_2 \\ \underline{t}' & 1 - t'a \end{bmatrix}$$

So we have, if we now denote each of the quantities referring to the whole lens with the subscript 1, 2

$$a_{1,2} = a_1 + a_2 - \underline{t}'a_1 a_2$$
$$b_{1,2} = 1 - \underline{t}'a_2$$
$$c_{1,2} = 1 - \underline{t}'a_1$$
$$d_{1,2} = -\underline{t}'$$

The location of the unit points for a number of cases is shown in Fig. 4-6.

THE THIN LENS

If we can assume that the thickness of a single lens is neglible compared to the focal length of this lens, it is customary, owing to the great simplifications it brings about, to take $\underline{t}' = 0$. This is called the "thin" lens. Introducing this condition into the equations above, we find

$$a_{1,2} = a_1 + a_2$$
$$b_{1,2} = c_{1,2} = 1$$
$$d_{1,2} = 0$$

It is easily shown that in this case both unit points coincide and we

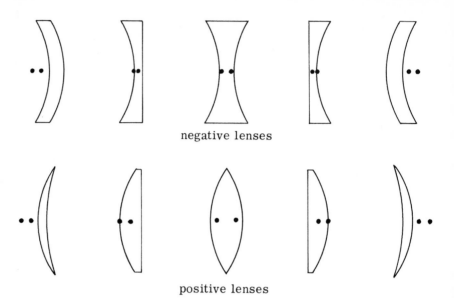

negative lenses

positive lenses

Fig. 4-6.   Position of unit points for various shapes of single lenses.

have a situation as shown in Fig. 4-7.

PARAXIAL RAYS AWAY FROM THE AXIS

From the way we derived the paraxial formulas, it would seem that we can use them only for rays traveling close to the axis. If we define a perfect system in such a way that the matrix

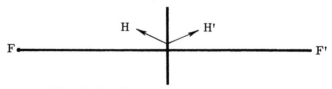

Fig. 4-7.   Unit points for a thin lens.

$$\begin{bmatrix} \dfrac{1}{\beta'} & -a \\ 0 & \beta' \end{bmatrix}$$

describes the image formation, it is clearly seen that all the actual rays will travel close to the path described by the paraxial laws. For a first approximation, we can thus use the paraxial laws to describe the rays farther away from the axis. The deviations of rays from the paths described by these paraxial laws are called aberrations.

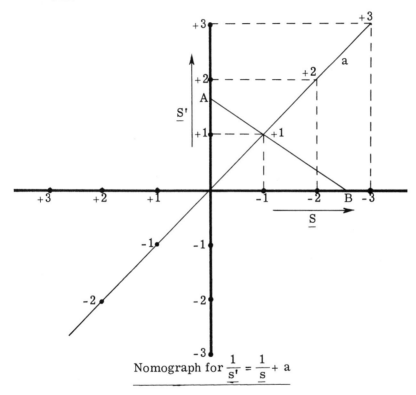

Nomograph for $\dfrac{1}{\underline{s'}} = \dfrac{1}{\underline{s}} + \underline{a}$

Fig. 4-8. Nomograph for object-image relationship.

The line AB (Fig. 4-8) represents $\underline{s} = -2.50$ and a power of $+1$, giving an image distance of $\underline{s'} = 1.67$. A mental picture of this nomograph is very helpful in acquiring a feeling for the object and image relationships.

GRAPHICAL CONSTRUCTION OF PARAXIAL RAYS

If the unit points and focal distances of an optical system are given, it is possible to find graphically the position of the image (Fig. 4-9) by constructing the paths of a few rays. To find the image of a point P it is necessary to find in the image space the intersection of two rays coming from P. There are three specific rays whose continuation in the image space is easily constructed.

a. If we take a ray through P parallel to the axis, we can consider this ray as coming from a point on the axis at infinity, and for this reason it has to go through the focal point F', being by definition the image of this point. In order to construct this ray in the image space we need one more point on this ray in the image space. The point Q, which is on the ray in the object space and in the object unit surface, is imaged in the image unit surface in a point Q' where HQ = H'Q' (definition of unit surfaces). We now have two points Q' and F' on the ray in the image space and thus a' is the ray.

b. If we take a ray through P and F in the object space which intersects the object unit plane at S, it is clear that from the definition of unit surfaces the ray has to go through S' where HS = H'S' and has to intersect the axis at a point at infinity (definition of object focal point), or in other words is parallel to the axis. Thus b' is the ray.

c. If our given lens system is in air, and therefore the nodal points coincide with the unit points, a ray going through the axial point of the object unit surface will go through the axial point of the image unit surface and the angle of the ray with the axis in the object space is equal to the angle of the ray with the axis in the image

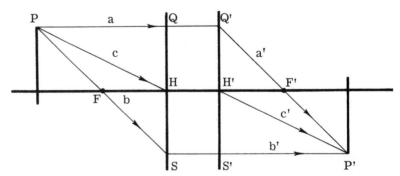

Fig. 4-9.   Construction of paraxial rays.

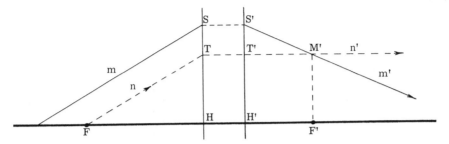

Fig. 4-10. Construction of an arbitrary paraxial ray.

space. So the ray PH will continue in image space as ray H'P' and
the angle PHF = the angle P'H'F'.

Any two of the above three rays suffice to find the image P' of
P.

To find the continuation of an arbitrary ray, we have to use a
slightly more complicated construction. Suppose m (Fig. 4-10) is
the ray for which we want to construct the continuation in the image
space. Again, the point S will be imaged in S'. To find a second
point on this ray in the image space, we procede as follows. Construct a ray n, parallel to m through the object focal point F. The
continuation of ray n is easily found as described in case (b). Now
the point at infinity on n will be imaged in the focal plane and thus
in M'. Now the ray m goes through the same point at infinity, of
which M' is the image. Thus the continuation of this ray should
also go through M'. Thus m' is the continuation in the image space
of m.

It is also possible to construct the unit points and focal points
for a system consisting of two given systems.

Suppose system 1 and system 2 (Fig. 4-11) are given. In order
to find the image focal point of the combined system, we must find
the intersection with the axis in the image space of a ray which
entered the system parallel to the axis. So by taking a ray a, parallel to the axis, we can easily construct the continuation a' of this
ray after passing through system 1. To find the continuation a'' of
this ray after passing system 2, we make use of the construction
described above for an arbitrary ray. The intersection of a'' with
the axis, the point F', is thus the image focal point of the combined
system.

To find the image unit surface, we make use of the fact that,
regardless of where object and image unit surfaces are located, the
intersection of a ray parallel to the axis with these surfaces will be

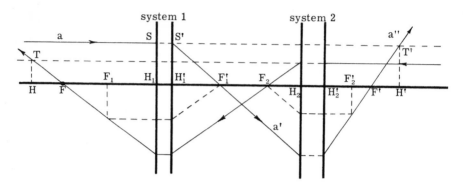

Fig. 4-11. Paraxial construction of cardinal points for a lens combination.

a distance H_1S away from the axis. Thus the ray a'' intersects the image unit surface at a point H_1S away from the axis and the only point on a'' fulfilling this condition is T'. So T'H' is the image unit surface and H' the image unit point. To find the object unit point and the object focal point, we use exactly the same procedure, starting, however, with a ray parallel to the axis and entering system 2 traveling from right to left, as shown in Fig. 4-11.

We have shown how it is possible to calculate the location of all the important points in an optical system and also how to construct the same points graphically.

Now let us try, as an example, to find these points in an actual

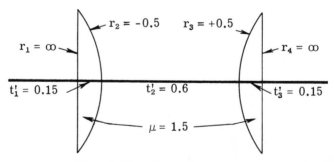

Fig. 4-12. Ramsden eyepiece.

system, e.g., that of a Ramsden eyepiece (Fig. 4-12). This system is obviously symmetrical and

$$t'_1 = t'_3 = \frac{0.15}{1.5} = 0.1$$

$$a_2 = a_3 = (1.5 - 1)\frac{1}{0.5} = 1$$

The matrices for this system are

$$\begin{bmatrix} 1 & 0 \\ 0 & 1 \end{bmatrix} \begin{bmatrix} 1 & 0 \\ 0.1 & 1 \end{bmatrix} \begin{bmatrix} 1 & -1 \\ 0 & 1 \end{bmatrix} \begin{bmatrix} 1 & 0 \\ 0.6 & 1 \end{bmatrix} \begin{bmatrix} 1 & -1 \\ 0 & 1 \end{bmatrix} \begin{bmatrix} 1 & 0 \\ 0.1 & 1 \end{bmatrix} \begin{bmatrix} 1 & 0 \\ 0 & 1 \end{bmatrix}$$

$$= \begin{bmatrix} 0.260 & -1.400 \\ 0.666 & 0.260 \end{bmatrix}$$

We find for the whole system

$$f' = \frac{1}{1.400} = 0.714$$

$$\ell'_F = \frac{0.26}{1.4} = 0.186$$

$$\ell_H = +0.529$$

$$\ell'_H = -0.529$$

This is a good example of a system in which the unit points fall inside the system and the image unit point falls to the left of the object unit point.

Let us now draw this system to scale and find the unit and focal points graphically. The object unit and focal points can be found by constructing a ray going from right to left through the system. Since this system is the same for light going in either direction we can locate these points without using this extra ray. This construction is shown in Fig. 4-13.

Further information is found in References 6, 7, 11, 12, 13, 15, 20, 21, 22, 37, 49, 88, 96, and 99.

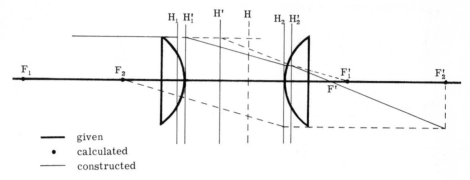

Fig. 4-13. Cardinal points of a Ramsden eyepiece.

Problem:

Given the lens system in Fig. 4-14, find the matrix for the system. Find the unit points and focal points for the system.

Answer:

$$\begin{bmatrix} 1.040 & -0.600 \\ 0.384 & 0.740 \end{bmatrix}$$

$$f' = +1.667$$

$$\ell_F = -1.733$$

$$\ell'_F = +1.233$$

$$\ell_H = -0.067$$

$$\ell'_H = -0.433$$

Problem:

Using the optical system in problem 2, Chap. 3, trace a ray, starting in the object plane, with coordinates, $x = +0.5$, $\alpha = 0.083$. The object plane is imaged with a magnification of $+2$.

Find the coordinates in the image plane.

Find object and image distances, s and s'.

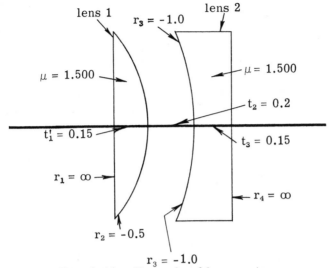

Fig. 4-14. Example of lens system.

Find ray coordinates for this ray after refraction at the last surface of the last lens.

Answers:

$$\begin{bmatrix} \underline{\alpha'} \\ x' \end{bmatrix} = \begin{bmatrix} 0.5 & -0.281 \\ 0 & 2 \end{bmatrix} \begin{bmatrix} -0.083 \\ +0.5 \end{bmatrix}$$

$$s = -1.781$$
$$s' = -3.561$$

$$\begin{bmatrix} \underline{\alpha'} \\ h' \end{bmatrix} = \begin{bmatrix} 0.508 & -0.281 \\ 2.512 & 0.580 \end{bmatrix} \begin{bmatrix} 1 & 0 \\ 0.028 & 1 \end{bmatrix} \begin{bmatrix} -0.083 \\ 0.5 \end{bmatrix}$$

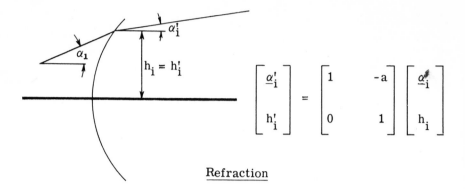

Refraction

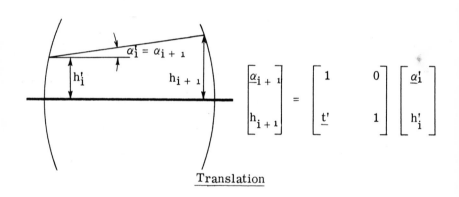

Translation

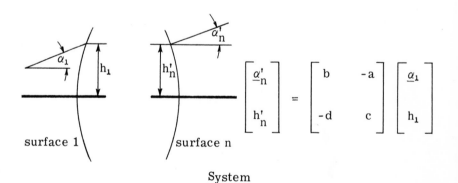

System

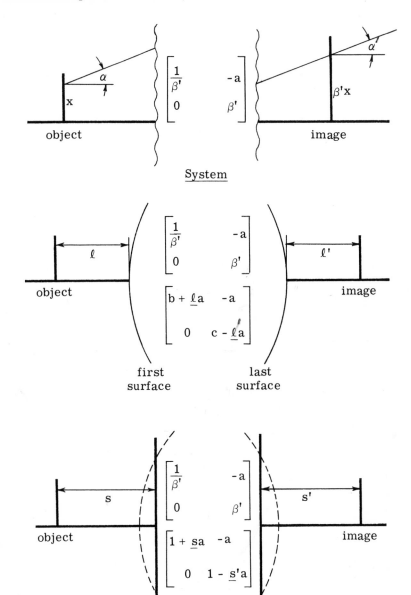

System

first surface   last surface

Unit Surfaces

Reduced angle $\underline{\alpha} = \mu\alpha$
Reduced distance along the axis $\underline{\ell} = \ell/\mu$ and $\underline{s} = s/\mu$
Distances perpendicular to the axis $\overline{h} = h$ and $\overline{x} = x$

Chapter 5

PUPILS OF OPTICAL SYSTEMS

In more complicated optical systems some rays might pass through the first few elements but miss the remaining elements.

To investigate this problem let us again take a system with axial symmetry. Let us assume that this system (Fig. 5-1) is broken up into two subsystems A and B and that we know the matrices M_A and M_B, which describe the paraxial ray transformations for rays going through the subsystems A and B.

Let us further assume that we put an aperture between the two systems and that the subsystems A and B are large enough to pass all the rays which pass our aperture. Now the question arises as

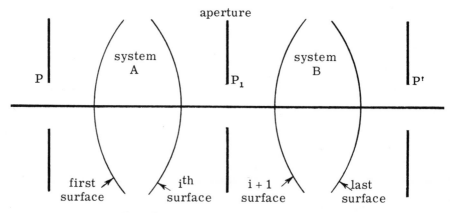

Fig. 5-1. Pupils of a lens system.

to which rays in object space are passed by the aperture.

In order to answer this question we image the aperture through system A into the object space. Now every point on the edge of our aperture is imaged in object space and so P_1 is imaged in P. Now every ray passing through P will go through P_1, and furthermore, by the same reasoning, all the rays passing through our aperture will have passed through the image of this aperture in object space.

The same procedure can be used to find which rays in image space are eliminated by our aperture. For this reason we image our aperture through subsystem B in image space or we take the image of our aperture in object space and image it through the whole system in the image space. These two procedures will, of course, give the same image in the image space. Again, all the rays passing through our aperture will go through its image in image space.

An optical system, in general, will consist of a number of elements and apertures. The edges of the elements can also be treated as limiting apertures. If we want to find out which aperture is limiting the bundle of rays passed by the system, we image every edge and aperture back into object space through all the lens elements preceding each edge or aperture in question. In this way we get a number of images in object space.

For a given object plane we will have an axial object point. The size of the bundle emerging from this point and passed by the optical system will be limited by that aperture whose image in object space is smallest, as seen from this axial object point. This limiting aperture is called the entrance pupil. By imaging this entrance pupil through the whole system into image space we find the exit pupil (Fig. 5-2).

It is clearly seen that the decision as to which aperture will be the entrance pupil depends on the position of the object plane. In Fig. 5-2 if the object plane is moved further to the left there will be a point where aperture 1, instead of aperture 2, limits the bundle.

It is also clear that, starting from the original object plane, bundles from a point-off axis could be limited by a different aperture or even more than one aperture. As a matter of fact, it is possible in some cases to find object points for which no rays at all will be passed by the system.

The ray from an off-axis object point through the axial point of the entrance pupil is called the principal ray for this object point. If the bundle of rays is limited only by the entrance pupil, this principal ray is in the center of the bundle.

If we look at the principal rays for points in the object further and further away from the axis, we will generally reach a point P where the principal ray for this point goes through the edge of an-

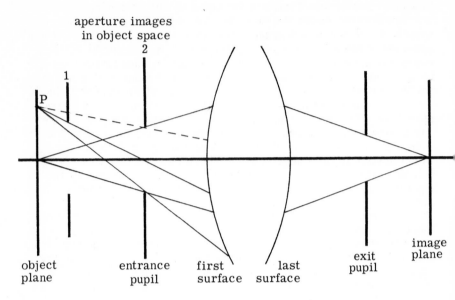

aperture images
in object space

Fig. 5-2.   Entrance and exit pupil.

other image of an aperture, in our case image 1. It is clearly seen
that all the rays coming from P above this principal ray will be cut
off by aperture 1 and all the rays below the principal ray will be
let through. A cross section through this bundle in the exit pupil
will have the form shown in Fig. 5-3. This effect is called vignetting.

It is clear that more than one aperture can cause vignetting for

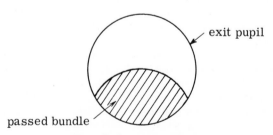

Fig. 5-3.   Vignetting.

the same bundle and the cross section can thus be more complicated than the one shown in Fig. 5-3.

It is also clear that less light is passed by a vignetted bundle
than one which is not vignetted. If the bundle of an object point is
completely vignetted we will have no image of this point and in this
way we will have a limit of the field of view of the system. The illumination in the image at this point of the field of view has dropped
to zero. For this reason it is customary to define the field of view
in such a way that the illumination at the edge is still approximately
one-half the value of the illumination at the center. This is usually
done by demanding that the principal ray for a point at the edge of
the field of view is still passed by our optical system. In Fig. 5-2
P will thus be the edge of the field of view. The aperture image 1,
which limits the field of view as defined above, is called the object
field stop. In the same way as we imaged the pupil, we can image
the object field stop through the whole system in the image space;
this image is called the image field stop.

It is seen that for the calculations of the positions of the images of the apertures in object space we need the matrices describing the first n elements of the system. From the way we calculate
the matrix of the whole system

$$M_{1,e} = M_e \cdot M_{e-1} \text{------} M_{n+1} \cdot M_n \cdot M_{n-1} \text{----} M_3 M_2 M_1$$

$$= M_e \cdot M_{e-1} \text{------} M_{n+1} \cdot M_n \cdot M_{n-1} \text{----} M_3 \cdot M_{1,2}$$

$$= M_e \cdot M_{e-1} \text{------} M_{n+1} \cdot M_{1,n}$$

etc.

we see that we already have all the necessary matrices calculated
while calculating the matrix for the whole system.

Let us take a periscope as an example. Suppose we want to
image an object located at A, Fig. 5-4, in the position B with a
magnification of +1. It is clear that this cannot be done with a single thin lens; owing to the magnification required, we have to locate
the object in the object unit surface, but then the image will be in
the same location. The next possibility is two thin lenses. Now
there are many solutions. Let us select, however, the case where
the first lens images the object with a magnification of -1 in image
1 and lens 2 images this again with a magnification of -1 in image
2. The powers of lenses 1 and 2 are not yet determined by these
requirements. It seems reasonable, however, to make them equal,
for this minimizes the power for each lens and aberrations will be
minimized. In that case the distance between the object and image

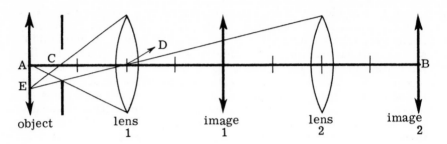

Fig. 5-4. Simple periscope.

for each lens is half the distance between A and B. Let us assume that the distance AB is 8 units. Then for each lens we have the following conditions.

(a) $\dfrac{1}{s'} = \dfrac{1}{s} + a$

(b) $\underline{s}' - \underline{s} = 4$

(c) $\beta' = \dfrac{\underline{s}'}{\underline{s}} = -1$

From (c) we get

$$\underline{s}' = -\underline{s}$$

From (b) we find

$$\underline{s}' = +2 \quad \text{and} \quad \underline{s} = -2$$

And then from (a) we find

$$a = +1$$

Let us now determine the entrance pupil and field of view of this system. To find these we have to image all the lens edges back into the object space.

The first lens edge (the lens being thin) is its own image. The position of the image of lens 2 can be found by considering lens 2 as an object for lens 1. Instead of imaging this lens in object space, we can consider this lens to be an image formed by lens 1 of an aperture in object space.

In doing so we find

$$0.25 = \frac{1}{\underline{s}} + 1$$

thus

$$\underline{s} = -1.333$$

If the lens diameter of each lens is d, the diameter of the image of lens 2 in object space is

$$0.333d$$

To find the entrance pupil we have to determine which aperture in the object space is smallest, as seen from A. It is clear that they are both the same because

$$\frac{AC}{0.333d} = \frac{AD}{d}$$

In this case we can regard either lens as the entrance pupil; or, in other words, the bundle from point A which is passed by lens 1 will also be the maximum bundle which can be passed by lens 2.

To find the field stop we have to select an entrance pupil. If we select lens 1 we find that the field of view is

$$2\,AE = AD\frac{0.333}{CD} = 0.5d$$

If we select lens 2 we find

$$2\,AE = AC\frac{d}{CD} = 0.5d$$

Thus we see that this gives us the same result in both cases, and we can select either one as the entrance pupil and the other as the

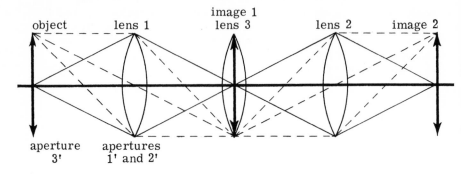

Fig. 5-5. Simple periscope with field lens.

field stop. We also see that the image size is limited to one-half the size of the lenses used, and this seems rather small.

We will now show that by using one more lens we can increase the field of view by a factor of two. If we insert a lens 3 (Fig. 5-5) of the same power and diameter as the others, midway between lenses 1 and 2, we see that this lens coincides with the image formed by lens 1 of the object and does not alter the position of the image formed by lens 2. If we now image the edges of all the lenses back in object space, we see that the image of lens 2 now falls on lens 1, thus coinciding with the image of lens 1. Lens 3 is imaged in the same position as the object. Now it is clear that all the apertures have a diameter d.

It is now evident that lenses 1 and 2 can again both be looked upon as forming the entrance pupil. However, the field stop is now the image of lens 3. The field of view now has a diameter equal to d.

Lens 3 is called a field lens. In this particular case, where the field stop coincides with the object, we notice that there is no vignetting and the illumination over the whole field is uniform.

SURVEY OF PHOTOMETRIC UNITS AND DEFINITIONS

Φ, Light Flux or Luminous Flux
German - Lichtstrom
French - flux lumineux

Definition
> The total visible energy emanating from a light source.

Unit
> Lumen (lm)

Photometric Definition
> At a wavelength of 5550 Å each watt of radiation corresponds to a light flux of 685 lm. From the sensitivity curve of the eye we find that at this wavelength its sensitivity is equal to 1. For a different wavelength λ, the sensitivity is V. Thus

$$\Phi = 685 \int_0^\infty V_\lambda P_\lambda \, d\lambda \qquad lm \qquad\qquad (5-1)$$

in which P_λ is the energy radiated at the wavelength in watts.

Old Definition
> One lumen is the light flux emanated in one steradian by a uniform point of light of one candle. (See definition of intensity of a source.) Thus a light source of one candle radiating equally in all directions emits 4π lm.

I, Intensity of a Source, Luminous Intensity, Candle Power
German - Lichtstarke
French - intensité lumineuse d'une source

Definition
> Luminous intensity is defined as the number of lumen per unit of solid angle (steradian) from a point source of light.

$$I = \frac{d\lambda}{d\omega} \qquad\qquad (5-2)$$

$$\Phi = \int_0^{4\pi} I \, d\omega \qquad\qquad (5-3)$$

Unit
> Candle (c) the new definition of a candle is 1/60 part of the luminous intensity of a black-body radiator of 1 cm² at the tempera-

Table 5-1

Conversion from ⬇ to ⟶	International candle (lumen per steradian) Pentaan candle English sperm candle	Carcel unit	Platinum candle	Heffner candle
International candle (lumen per steradian) Pentaan candle English sperm candle	1	0.104	1.020	1.11
Carcel unit	9.6	1	9.81	10.7
Platinum candle	0.980	0.102	1	1.088
Heffner candle	0.90	0.0936	0.919	1

ture of melting platinum (2043°C). (See Table 5-1.)

E, Illuminance, Illumination, Light Flux Density
German - Beleuchtungs-Starke
French - éclairement

<u>Definition</u>
    Illuminance is defined as the incoming light flux per unit or area.

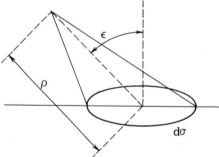

$$E = \frac{d\Phi}{d\sigma} \qquad (5\text{-}4)$$

$$d\omega = \frac{d\sigma \cos \epsilon}{\rho^2} \qquad (5\text{-}5)$$

Table 5-2

Conversion from to→	Foot-candle	Meter-candle (lux)	Phot
Foot-candle	1	10.764	1.0764×10^3
Meter-candle (lux)	0.092902	1	10^{-4}
Phot	929.02	10^4	1

Thus

$$d\Phi = I \, d\omega = I\frac{d\sigma \, \cos \epsilon}{\rho^2} \tag{5-6}$$

and

$$E = \frac{I \cos \epsilon}{\rho^2} \tag{5-7}$$

Units (Table 5-2)

Foot-candle = lumen per square foot (lm/ft²)
Meter-candle = lux = lm/m²
Phot = lm/cm²

B, Luminance or Brightness

German - Leuchdichte, Flächenhelle
French - brillance (éclat)

Definition

The brightness of a light emitting surface in a given direction is defined as light flux in this direction emitted by one unit of area divided by its apparent area.

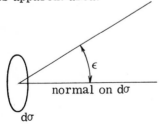

$$B = \frac{I}{d\sigma \, \cos \epsilon} \tag{5-8}$$

Table 5-3

Conversion from to →	Stilb (c/cm²)	Lambert (1/π = c/cm²)	c/in.²	c/m²	Apostilbe (1/π = c/m²)
Stilb (c/cm²)	1	3.1416	6.45	10^4	31416
Lambert (1/π = c/cm²)	0.3183	1	2.054	3183	10^4
c/in.²	0.155	0.48695	1	1550	4870
Apostilbe (1/π = c/m²)	3.183×10^{-3}	10^{-4}	2.054×10^{-4}	0.3183	1
c/m²	10^{-4}	3.1416×10^{-4}	6.45×10^{-4}	1	3.1416

Units (Table 5-3)

Stilb = candle/cm²
Apostilbe = $1/\pi$ = candle/m²
Lambert = $1/\pi$ = candle/cm²

If we assume that the surface radiates the same light flux in all directions this unit can be expressed in lumen/unit area. This is done quite often with the Lambert and under these conditions we have

Lambert = lm/cm²

For this condition the conversion table is as given in Table 5-4.

Table 5-4

Conversion from to →	Lambert (lm/cm²)	Lumen per square inch	Lumen per square foot
Lambert (lm/cm²)	1	6.45	930.25
Lumen per square inch	0.155	1	147.62
Lumen per square foot	1.076×10^{-3}	6.77×10^{-2}	1

The Basic Photometric Law

From the equation

$$I = E \, d\sigma \, \cos \epsilon = \frac{d\Phi}{d\omega} \tag{5-9}$$

it follows that

$$d\Phi = E \, d\omega \, d\sigma \, \cos \epsilon \tag{5-10}$$

A BRIEF SUMMARY OF LIGHT INTENSITY LEVELS

Illumination by sunlight at noon
    Summer: 80,000 lux
    Winter: 20,000 lux

After sunset (average at our latitude)

Sun height, deg	0	-1	-2	-3	-4	-5	-6	-8	-11	-17
Illumination, lux	400	250	115	40	14	4	1	0.1	0.01	0.001

Magnitude of stars
    The ratio of light intensity between two stars of successive magnitude is 2.512.

Illumination by the moon
    Full moon is 0.20 lux.
    First and last quarter is 0.02 lux.

The sensitivity of the eye
    A fully adapted eye can see 10^{-9} lux. This is equivalent to seeing a lighted candle at a distance of 20 miles. A white cloud is 10 times brighter than the blue sky. The sun's disk is 300,000 times brighter than the blue sky and it is 500,000 times brighter than the moon's disk.

Desirable artificial illumination levels
     100-200 lux: Reading of normal print, work where it is not
                         necessary to see fine details.
     200-300 lux: Sewing on white material, reading of newspapers,
                         writing over extended periods.
     300-500 lux: Drawing and fine work over long periods of time.
    500-1000 lux: Sewing and mending of dark materials.
    1000-2000 lux: Precision work over extended periods, drawing
                         of fine details, and fine repair work (watchmak-
                         ing, etc.).

Brightness of Images Formed by Optical Systems

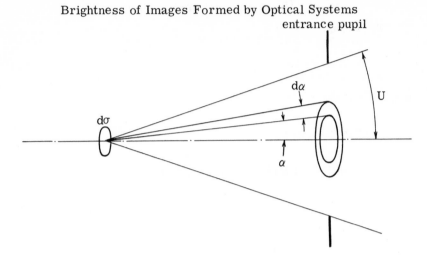

Fig. 5-6.   Light entering an optical system.

Brightness of Images Formed by Optical Systems

In Fig. 5-6 let $d\sigma$ be an element of area of the object.   The light flux $d\Phi$ into the element of solid angle $d\omega$, defined by a double cone of aperture α to $\alpha + d\alpha$, is, according to Eq. (5-11),

$$d\Phi = B \cos \alpha \, d\sigma \, d\omega \tag{5-11}$$

in which B is the luminance of the object.

Since the solid angle $d\omega$ is equal to the area of a unit sphere contained between the two cones, we have

$$d\omega = 2\pi \sin \alpha \, d\alpha \tag{5-12}$$

Therefore

$$d\Phi = 2\pi B \cos \alpha \sin \alpha \, d\alpha \, d\sigma \tag{5-13}$$

If the total cone admitted by the optical system has an angle U, we can calculate the total light flux going into the system.   We find

$$\Phi_U = 2\pi \int_0^U B \cos \alpha \sin \alpha \, d\alpha \, d\sigma = \pi B \, d\sigma \sin^2 U \qquad (5\text{-}14)$$

In calculating the flux $\Phi_{U'}$, which goes through an area $d\sigma'$ in the image space, the argument is exactly the same as the one above. We find

$$\Phi_{U'} = \pi B' \, d\sigma' \sin^2 U' \qquad (5\text{-}15)$$

in which B' is the luminance of the image.

In principle Φ_U is equal to $\Phi_{U'}$, when there are no reflection and transmission losses. When we want to take these losses into account, we multiply Φ_U by a factor τ, which is >0 and <1 and is called the transmission factor of the system. Then

$$\Phi_{U'} = \tau \Phi_U \qquad (5\text{-}16)$$

or

$$B' \, d\sigma' \sin^2 U' = \tau B \, d\sigma \sin^2 U \qquad (5\text{-}17)$$

If the system is aberration-free we have

$$d\sigma = dx \, dy \qquad d\sigma' = dx' \, dy'$$
$$dx' = \beta' \, dx \qquad dy' = \beta' \, dy$$
$$d\sigma' = \beta'^2 \, d\sigma$$

and according to the sine condition

$$\frac{\mu' \sin U'}{\mu \sin U} = \frac{1}{\beta'} \qquad (5\text{-}18)$$

Thus we find

$$B' \beta'^2 \frac{\mu^2 \sin^2 U}{\mu'^2 \beta'^2} = \tau B \, d\sigma \sin^2 U \qquad (5\text{-}19)$$

or

$$B' = \tau B \left(\frac{\mu'}{\mu}\right)^2 \qquad (5\text{-}20)$$

So if we neglect the transmission losses in the system, the luminance of the image is always equal to the luminance of the object.

In applications where the total energy in the image is important, we can use the above results. In other applications (photography, etc.), the total energy is not as important as the light flux density or illuminance E'. Here we find

$$E' = \frac{\Phi'}{d\sigma'} = \pi B' \sin^2 U' \tag{5-21}$$

If again the system is aberration-free, we can use the sine condition and write

$$E' = \pi B' \sin^2 U' = \tau B \frac{\sin^2 U}{\beta'^2} \pi \tag{5-22}$$

In most photographic objectives the pupil is close to the lens and the object is at infinity so both sin U and β' are zero. In order to calculate E' we have to calculate the

$$\lim_{U \to 0} \frac{\sin^2 U}{\beta'^2}$$

If s is very large and by consequence sin U very small, we can re-place sin U by tan U and this again by ρ/s, where ρ is the radius of the entrance pupil. According to Eq. (4-8) we have

$$\frac{s'}{s} = \beta'$$

Thus we find

$$E' = \tau B \frac{\rho^2 s^2}{s^2 s'^2} = \tau B \left(\frac{\rho}{f'}\right)^2 \pi \tag{5-23}$$

The F number (F*) is defined as

$$F^* = \frac{f'}{2\rho} \tag{5-24}$$

Thus

$$E' = \frac{1}{4} \frac{\tau B \pi}{F^{*2}} \tag{5-25}$$

In practical use a camera lens diaphragm is usually marked in such a way that each successive stop changes the E' by a factor of two.

American System

F*	1.4	2	2.8	4	5.6	8	11	16	22	32
F*2	1.96	4	7.84	16	31.4	64	121	256	484	1024

   In Europe a slightly different set of numbers is used. We see
also that the above definition does not include the value of the transmission (τ) of the optical system. The value of τ can obviously
vary considerably for different lenses. This is why the T-stop values were recently introduced. In this way we mark the stop values
in such a way that the illuminance of the image is equal to the illuminance of a system with the above F* but with a transmission
equal to 1.
   The above discussion only holds for a small object centered
around the axis of the lens. When we go off axis the illuminance in
the image generally decreases. We can estimate this variation in
illuminance as follows.
   Let, in Fig. 5-7, the angle that a ray makes with the axis,
passing through the center of the diaphragm, be ψ in the object
space, ψ_p in the space where the diaphragm is located, and ψ' in
the image space. Let an element of the image in the point P' have
a height dx' and a width dy'. We shall write $d\psi_p$ for the change in
ψ_p when P' travels over a distance dx' in the plane of drawing.
When P' travels over a distance dy' perpendicular to the plane of
drawing, the central ray passing through the diaphragm will rotate
over an angle dy' sin ψ_p/x'. So the solid angle $d\omega$ subtended by the
image element dx' dy', as seen from the center of the diaphragm,
is

$$d\omega = d\psi_p \frac{dy'}{x'} \sin \psi_p$$

When B is the luminance of the object in the object point P, σ the

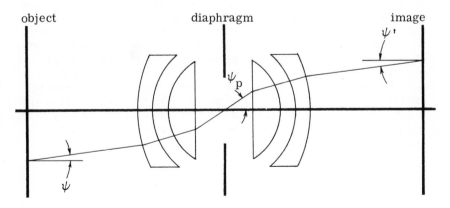

Fig. 5-7

area of the opening in the diaphragm, and τ the transmission of the system, we find for the total light flux $d\phi$ arriving at the surface element dx' dy'

$$d\phi = \tau B\sigma \, \cos \psi_p \, d\psi_p \, \frac{dy'}{x'} \sin \psi_p$$

provided that σ is small. Consequently, the illuminance in the point P' is given by

$$E' = \tau B\sigma \, \sin \psi_p \, \cos \psi_p \frac{1}{x'} \frac{d\psi_p}{dx'}$$

The trigonometrical relation

$$\frac{d}{dx} \tan^2 \psi = 2 \frac{\sin \psi}{\cos^3 \psi}$$

allows us to write for this expression

$$E' = \tau B\sigma \, \cos^4 \psi \frac{d \, (\tan^2 \psi)}{d \, (x'^2)} \frac{d \, (\sin^2 \psi_p)}{d \, (\sin^2 \psi)}$$

If the lens is used with the object at infinity and there is no distortion, x' is proportional to $\tan \psi$ and the factor $d \, (\tan^2 \psi)/d(x'^2)$ reduces to a constant. The image of the diaphragm formed by the front part of the lens is the entrance pupil; if this entrance pupil image is free of coma, then, according to Abbe's sine law, the last factor also reduces to a constant. We see that, when all these assumptions are fulfilled, the illuminance in the image plane is proportional to the fourth power of the cosine of the field angle in the object space. For large field angles this would lead to very low levels of illumination; for that reason the image formation of the pupil by the front part of the system must in wide-angle lenses be affected with a large amount of coma so as to counteract this cosine to the fourth law. A further reduction of the illumination may occur, due to "vignetting," i.e., rays being intercepted by obstructions other than the diaphragm.

For further information see References 46, 51, and 91.

Chapter 6

SOME REMARKS ABOUT REAL RAYS

GRAPHICAL CONSTRUCTION OF A NONPARAXIAL REFRACTED RAY

In Fig. 6-1, C is the center of curvature of a refracting surface with radius r. Let us take a ray EA incident at A on the refracting surface. At this point construct a circle with its center at
C and tangent to this incoming ray (in our case at point B). We will
call its radius ρ and

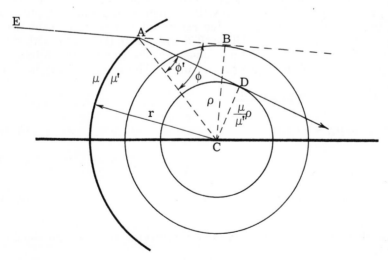

Fig. 6-1. First graphical construction of refracted ray.

BC = ρ

If we now construct a circle with radius

$$CD = \frac{\mu}{\mu'}\rho$$

we find the refracted ray as a line tangent to this last circle and starting in A (the line AD). From Fig. 6-1 we see that

$$\sin \phi = \frac{\rho}{r} \quad \text{and} \quad \sin \phi' = \frac{\mu\rho}{\mu'r}$$

And from this we determine

$$\sin \phi' = \frac{\mu}{\mu'} \sin \phi$$

which is in accordance with Snell's law

This construction is easily carried out with the aid of proportional dividers. The pivot point is adjusted in such a way that the relationship between the two openings is μ/μ'.

There is, however, another well-known graphical construction (Fig. 6-2). Again we have a refracting surface with radius r and center C. We now draw two auxiliary circles with radii $(\mu'/\mu)r$ and $(\mu/\mu')r$. In order to construct the refracted continuation of the incident ray DP we continue DP until it intersects the circle with radius $(\mu'/\mu)r$ in point B. We now construct the line CB which intersects the circle with radius $(\mu/\mu')r$ in A. The refracted ray is then PA.

We shall first prove that

$$\triangle CPA \sim \triangle CBP \tag{6-1}$$

We see that

$$\angle PCA = \angle BCP \tag{6-2}$$

If the above triangles are similar the following relationship should exist:

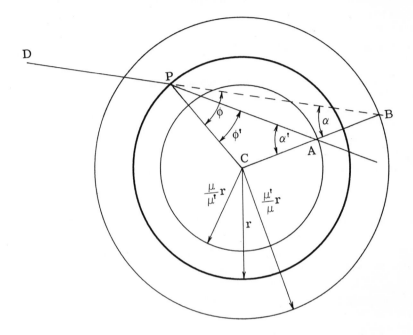

Fig. 6-2. Second graphical construction of refracted ray.

$$\frac{CP}{CB} = \frac{CA}{CP}$$

or   (6-3)

$$CP^2 = CB \cdot CA$$

And by substitution

$$r^2 = \frac{\mu'}{\mu} r \cdot \frac{\mu}{\mu'} r$$

$$= r^2$$

Thus the relationship in (6-3) is proved, and we see that the triangles are similar.

Now we must prove that in this case the ray obeys Snell's law. From Snell's law it follows that the normal (PC), incident (DP), and refracted (PA) rays are in one plane.   Then we have to prove that in the above construction

$$\mu \sin \phi = \mu' \sin \phi'$$

From the relationship in Eq. (6-1) we see that

$$\angle CBP = \angle CPA$$
$$\angle CPA = \phi'$$

Therefore in triangle CPB

$$\frac{PC}{\sin \phi'} = \frac{CB}{\sin \phi}$$

so

$$PC \sin \phi = CB \sin \phi'$$

and by substitution

$$\not{C} \sin \phi = \frac{\mu'}{\mu} \not{C} \sin \phi'$$

Therefore,

$$\mu \sin \phi = \mu' \sin \phi'$$

We have thus proved that in constructing the refracted ray in the above way, the ray obeys Snell's law

APLANATIC POINTS FOR A SINGLE REFRACTING SURFACE

If a point is imaged by a single surface, the image is generally afflicted with aberrations.   There are, however, certain points which are imaged aberration-free in monochromatic light.   These sets of conjugate points are called aplanatic points.

We shall see that there are three such collections of points.

1.   Let us consider a point on a refracting surface.   The image of this point will coincide with the object point, and the image formation will be aberration-free (Fig. 6-3).   For the axial points

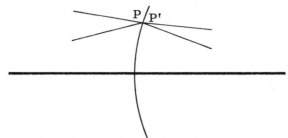

Fig. 6-3.   Object point on the refracting surface.

we have

$$\ell = \ell' = 0$$

or   (6-4)

$$\underline{\ell} = \underline{\ell}' = 0$$

2.   If an object point is located at the center of curvature of a refracting surface, we again have an aplanatic point.   In this case all rays in the object space converging toward this point will, after refraction, converge again toward the same point because for all these rays the incident angle ϕ equals 0.   For this point we find

$$\ell = \ell' = r \tag{6-5}$$

3.   If we again consider our second construction for a refracted ray (Fig. 6-2), we will notice that all rays which converge in the object space toward point B will converge in the image space toward point A and again the points A and B are aplanatic.   As a matter of fact the whole sphere with radius $(\mu'/\mu)r$ is imaged on the sphere $(\mu/\mu')r$ without aberrations.   For the axial points we then have

$$\ell = \frac{\mu'}{\mu} r \quad \text{and} \quad \ell' = \frac{\mu}{\mu'} r \tag{6-6}$$

Satisfy yourself that the above axial aplanatic points satisfy the paraxial image equations.

RAY TRACING FORMULAS

At this point we should normally take up the ray tracing formulas. These formulas enable the designer to follow a ray through an optical system. One way of doing this would be to use formulas for calculating A and $\underline{T}'$ for a general case. See p. 15, where simple cases were treated.

There are, however, many methods of following a ray through an optical system and the one to be used will depend, to a large extent, on the type of equipment available. It is pointless to use log formulas if we have an I.B.M., and vice versa, so we shall omit these formulas.

Chapter 7

COLOR ABBERATIONS

OPTICAL GLASS

We have seen that in all our formulas (even the ones for paraxial optics) one of the terms used is the refractive index μ. The refractive index of a medium is a function of the wavelength of the light refracted by it. Since we shall normally be using optical glass for our refracting medium, let us look into its properties with respect to wavelength.

It is usual to give the refractive index for certain wavelengths. These wavelengths are emitted by certain elements. Sources emitting these wavelengths are readily available. The wavelengths most commonly used and the elements by which these lines are emitted are listed in Table 7-1.

It was customary in former times to use the sodium D line because it was readily available. However, since this is a doublet it has now been agreed to replace it by the helium d line.

The units in which these wavelengths are measured are angstrom units (1 $\overset{\circ}{A}$ = 10^{-10} meter). Wavelengths measured with respect to internationally agreed-upon standard wavelengths are referred to in international angstrom units (I $\overset{\circ}{A}$).

To make the calculation of color aberrations easier in certain cases (as we shall see later), most tables of glass characteristics include the ν value (nu value).

$$\nu = \frac{\mu_d - 1}{\mu_F - \mu_C} \tag{7-1}$$

Table 7-1. Common Spectrum Lines Used in Measuring Glass

Name of line	Emitted by	Wavelength in IÅ	Color
A'	K	7699.01* 7666.94	Red
b	He	7065.19	Red
C	H	6562.80	Red
D	Na	5895.932* 5889.965	Yellow
d	He	5875.62	Yellow
e	Hg	5460.74	Green
F	H	4861.33	Blue
g	Hg	4358.34	Violet
g'	H	4340.465	Violet
h	Hg	4046.56	Violet

*For practical purposes the average wavelength for the A' line is considered to be 7680.1 and for the D line 5892.6.

Table 7-2 is a summary of available optical glasses. Some new glasses are listed in Table 7-3. A graphical plot of the area in which these glasses are available is given in Fig. 7-1.

From Eq. (7-1) we see that the larger the ν value the less the dispersion of the medium. Where there is no dispersion at all, the ν value = ∞ ($\nu = \infty$).

It is customary to indicate a glass with one number, such as 517/607 or 517-607. The first three numbers are the first three numbers after the decimal point of the refractive index and the last three numbers give the ν value, omitting the decimal point. Thus the above glass has a refractive index of 1.517 and a ν value of 60.7.

THE COLOR ABERRATION MATRICES

The most simple manner to calculate color aberration of any lens system is by the use of matrices. Now, however, we must use the matrix description of differentials. For an outline of this

Table 7-2. Some Typical Optical Glasses

	Type[a]	Code	b	C	d	e	F	g	h
1	FC	466/643	1.46203	1.46333	1.46556	1.46732	1.47057	1.47444	1.47765
2	BSC	517/638	1.51273	1.51418	1.51666	1.51858	1.52225	1.52657	1.5301
3	C1	517/607	1.51265	1.51418	1.51678	1.51881	1.52269	1.52727	1.5311
4	C2	523/592	1.51898	1.52052	1.52321	1.52530	1.52936	1.53418	1.53816
5	LBaC1	540/595	1.53661	1.53818	1.54095	1.54311	1.54727	1.55221	1.55631
6	LBaC2	572/575	1.56778	1.56947	1.57250	1.57486	1.57943	1.58488	1.58942
7	DBC1	589/612	1.58429	1.58598	1.58894	1.59124	1.59560	1.60077	1.60504
8	DBC2	620/502	1.61411	1.61620	1.61990	1.62284	1.62854	1.63543	1.64123
9	LBaF	589/511	1.58336	1.58529	1.58875	1.59148	1.59681	1.60324	1.60865
10	LF	578/432	1.57192	1.57413	1.57811	1.58130	1.58752	1.59513	1.60170
11	BaF	606/439	1.59924	1.60552	1.60562	1.60889	1.61531	1.62318	1.62991
12	DF1	620/363	1.61250	1.61534	1.62035	1.62440	1.63241	1.64237	1.65099
13	DF2	654/338	1.64571	1.64880	1.65446	1.65904	1.66817	1.67956	1.68950
14	DBaF	668/419	1.6605	1.66284	1.66755	1.67134	1.67878	1.68793	1.69579
15	EDF	701/302	1.68765	1.69427	1.70100	1.70648	1.71748	1.73135	1.7437
16	CF	530/514	1.52494	1.52670	1.52983	1.53227	1.53700	1.54268	1.54743

[a]The abbreviations under "Type" mean the following:

1	Fluor crown	6	Light barium crown
2	Borosilicate crown	7	Dense barium crown
3	Crown	8	Dense barium crown
4	Crown	9	Light barium flint
5	Light barium crown	10	Light flint

11	Barium flint
12	Dense flint
13	Dense flint
14	Dense barium flint
15	Extra dense flint
16	Crown flint

Table 7-3.   Index of Refraction for Some New Glasses

Origin	Type	A'		C	D	F	G'
NBS[a]	610/620	62.0	....	1.6067	1.6096	1.6165	1.6220
NBS	639/597	59.7	....	1.6363	1.6395	1.6470	1.6531
NBS	656/582	58.2	....	1.6522	1.6555	1.6634	1.6698
EK[b]	EK-110	56.2	1.68877	1.69313	1.69680	1.70554	1.71255
NBS	673/562	56.2	....	1.6697	1.6733	1.6817	1.6885
Hay[c]	651/558	55.8	....	1.64757	1.65100	1.65924	1.66590
NBS	682/553	55.3	....	1.6782	1.6819	1.6906	1.6976
NBS	705/540	54.0	....	1.7011	1.7049	1.7142	1.7216
NBS	714/531	53.1	....	1.7103	1.7143	1.7238	1.7315
Hay	671/520	52.0	....	1.66724	1.67100	1.68018	1.68772
EK	EK-210	51.2	1.72482	1.72979	1.73400	1.74413	1.75235
Corn'g[d]	8313	47.8	....	1.69639	1.70065	1.71104	....
EK	EK-330	47.2	1.74499	1.75043	1.75510	1.76643	1.77571
EK	EK-310	46.4	1.73491	1.74033	1.74500	1.75638	1.76577
EK	EK-320	45.8	1.73432	1.73978	1.74450	1.75603	1.76557
EK	EK-450	41.8	1.79180	1.79814	1.80370	1.81738	1.82880
EK	EK-448	41.1	1.86714	1.87420	1.88040	1.89564	1.90827

[a] NBS, National Bureau of Standards.
[b] EK, Eastman Kodak Company.
[c] Hay, Hayward Scientific Glass Corp.
[d] Corn'g, Corning Glass Works.

process see p. 94.
    It is clear that we again have to consider two types of matrices, one for refraction and one for translation.

Refraction

    The matrix for refraction is

$$\begin{bmatrix} 1 & -(a + da) \\ 0 & 1 \end{bmatrix} = \begin{bmatrix} 1 & -a \\ 0 & 1 \end{bmatrix} + \begin{bmatrix} 0 & -da \\ 0 & 0 \end{bmatrix}$$

$$a = \frac{\mu' - \mu}{r} \quad \text{and} \quad da = \frac{d\mu' - d\mu}{r} \tag{7-2}$$

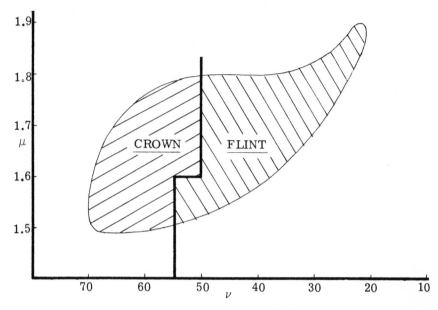

Fig. 7-1.   Available optical glasses.

Translation

The matrix for translation is

$$\begin{bmatrix} 1 & 0 \\ \underline{t}' + d\underline{t}' & 1 \end{bmatrix} = \begin{bmatrix} 1 & 0 \\ \underline{t}' & 1 \end{bmatrix} + \begin{bmatrix} 0 & 0 \\ d\underline{t}' & 0 \end{bmatrix}$$

$$\underline{t}' = \frac{t'}{\mu'}$$

Therefore

$$d\underline{t}' = -\frac{t'}{\mu'^2}\, d\mu' = -\underline{t}'\,\frac{d\mu'}{\mu'} \tag{7-3}$$

These matrices enable one to calculate the color aberrations of any lens system. We shall now look into some specific cases.

Thin Lens

We find for the normal matrix

$$\begin{bmatrix} b_{1,2} & -a_{1,2} \\ -d_{1,2} & c_{1,2} \end{bmatrix} = \begin{bmatrix} 1 & -a_2 \\ 0 & 1 \end{bmatrix} \begin{bmatrix} 1 & -a_1 \\ 0 & 1 \end{bmatrix} = \begin{bmatrix} 1 & -(a_2 + a_1) \\ 0 & 1 \end{bmatrix}$$

For the matrix describing the color aberrations we find

$$\begin{bmatrix} db_{1,2} & -da_{1,2} \\ -dd_{1,2} & dc_{1,2} \end{bmatrix} = \begin{bmatrix} 1 & -a_2 \\ 0 & 1 \end{bmatrix} \begin{bmatrix} 0 & -da_1 \\ 0 & 0 \end{bmatrix}$$

$$+ \begin{bmatrix} 0 & -da_2 \\ 0 & 0 \end{bmatrix} \begin{bmatrix} 1 & -a_1 \\ 0 & 1 \end{bmatrix}$$

$$= \begin{bmatrix} 0 & -da_1 \\ 0 & 0 \end{bmatrix} + \begin{bmatrix} 0 & -da_2 \\ 0 & 0 \end{bmatrix}$$

$$= \begin{bmatrix} 0 & -(da_1 + da_2) \\ 0 & 0 \end{bmatrix}$$

or

$$db_{1,2} = dc_{1,2} = dd_{1,2} = 0 \tag{7-4}$$

$$da_{1,2} = da_1 + da_2 \tag{7-5}$$

With the help of Eq. (7-2) (remembering that $d\mu$ for air equals 0) and calling the index of refraction for the first lens μ and its radii r_1 and r_2 we find

$$da_{1,2} = \frac{d\mu}{r_1} + \frac{-d\mu}{r_2}$$

If we now take

$$d\mu = \mu_F - \mu_C$$

or introduce the ν value

$$\nu = \frac{\mu_d - 1}{\mu_F - \mu_C} = \frac{\mu_d - 1}{d\mu}$$

or   (7-6)

$$d\mu = \frac{\mu_d - 1}{\nu}$$

then

$$da_{1,2} = \frac{\mu_d - 1}{\nu} \left(\frac{1}{r_1} - \frac{1}{r_2} \right) = \frac{a_{1,2}}{\nu} \tag{7-7}$$

or

$$\frac{da_{1,2}}{a_{1,2}} = \frac{1}{\nu} \tag{7-8}$$

Now

$$f'_{1,2} = \frac{1}{a_{1,2}}$$

$$df'_{1,2} = \frac{da_{1,2}}{a^2_{1,2}} = -\frac{1}{\nu a_{1,2}}$$

or

$$\frac{df'_{1,2}}{f'_{1,2}} = -\frac{1}{\nu} \tag{7-9}$$

For a lens of crown glass (C1 of Table 7-2) we find

$$df'_{1,2} = -\frac{f'_{1,2}}{60.7}$$

However, for a lens of flint glass (701/302) we find

$$df'_{1,2} = -\frac{f'_{1,2}}{30.2}$$

It is clear that by using the ν value we get values which relate to color differences between the F and c lines. If one wants to correct the system for two other wavelengths, say λ_1 and λ_2, we have to calculate our own ν value given by

$$\nu = \frac{\mu_\lambda - 1}{\mu_{\lambda_1} - \mu_{\lambda_2}} \tag{7-10}$$

where λ is a wavelength between λ_1 and λ_2.

Example
    Let us take a lens with a power of +2 made from glass with a ν value of 60 and find df'.

We have

$$a = +2$$

$$\nu = 60$$

We know that

$$f' = 0.5$$

and

$$df' = -\frac{f'}{\nu}$$

Therefore

$$df' = -\frac{0.5}{60}$$

$$= -\frac{1}{120}$$

Thus we see that for any lens with a power of +2 and a ν value of 60, the (F) line will focus at a point nearer the lens than will the (C) line by a distance of 1/120 length unit (Fig. 7-2).

Let us now consider the problem of finding the size of the blur circle, or the circle of confusion, of a thin lens.

$$\begin{bmatrix} \alpha' \\ x' \end{bmatrix} = \begin{bmatrix} b + \underline{\ell}a & -a \\ \underline{\ell}\ell'a + \underline{\ell}'b - \underline{\ell}c - d & c - \underline{\ell}'a \end{bmatrix} \begin{bmatrix} \alpha \\ x \end{bmatrix}$$

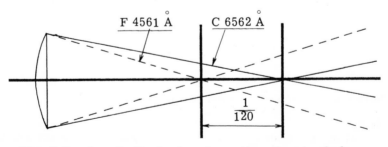

Fig. 7-2. Longitudinal color aberration of a simple lens.

We can now introduce the color aberrations to this equation and we have

$$\begin{bmatrix} d\underline{\alpha}' \\ dx' \end{bmatrix} = \begin{bmatrix} db + \underline{\ell}\ da & -da \\ \underline{\ell}\underline{\ell}'\ da + \underline{\ell}'\ db - \underline{\ell}\ dc - dd & dc - \underline{\ell}'\ da \end{bmatrix} \begin{bmatrix} \underline{\alpha} \\ x \end{bmatrix} \quad (7\text{-}14)$$

We know that for a thin lens

$$b = c = 1$$

and

$$d = 0$$

and

$$db = 0$$
$$dc = 0$$
$$dd = 0$$

Our matrix [Eq. (7-14)] now reads

$$\begin{bmatrix} d\underline{\alpha}' \\ dx' \end{bmatrix} = \begin{bmatrix} \underline{\ell}\ da & -da \\ \underline{\ell}\underline{\ell}'\ da & -\underline{\ell}'\ da \end{bmatrix} \begin{bmatrix} \underline{\alpha} \\ x \end{bmatrix} \quad (7\text{-}15)$$

This matrix will allow us to calculate dx' as a function of the object point (x) and the angle of the ray ($\underline{\alpha}$). This gives us the size of the blur circle directly.

For any given wavelength an optical system has a certain power. This means that for any given object distance $\underline{s}$ we shall find an image distance $\underline{s}'$. However, for different wavelengths we will have different image distances. If the object is an image formed by another lens with color aberration, $\underline{s}$ will also be a function of wavelength. To investigate the relation between $\underline{s}$, $\underline{s}'$, and a as a function of wavelength we differentiate the image equation.

We know that

$$\frac{1}{\underline{s}'} = \frac{1}{\underline{s}} + a$$

Therefore

$$-\frac{ds'}{\underline{s}'^2} = -\frac{ds}{\underline{s}^2} + da \quad (7\text{-}16)$$

Let us take as an example a negative lens with a power of -1 and a ν value of 30. Let the object for this lens be the image formed by the lens in the example on p. 81. Let us locate the negative lens behind the positive one with a distance zero between them. This gives us for the negative lens

$$s = +0.5 \quad \text{and} \quad da = -0.008$$

We know that

$$a = -1 \quad \text{and} \quad da = \underline{a}$$

so

$$da = -0.03333$$

We now get

$$-\frac{ds'}{s'^2} = +4(0.00833) - 0.03333$$

therefore

$$ds' = 0$$

Thus we find that we can start with an object which has color aberrations and finish with a color-free image. The general discussion of the thin systems without color aberrations will follow after a discussion of the single thick lens.

A Single Thick Lens

We have found that we always have color aberrations with a single thin lens. Now let us see whether or not we can correct for these aberrations with a properly designed thick lens.

By a thick lens we mean one in which $\underline{t}$ is not negligible compared to the focal length.

The normal matrix describing this system is

$$\begin{bmatrix} 1 & -a_2 \\ 0 & 1 \end{bmatrix} \begin{bmatrix} 1 & 0 \\ \underline{t}' & 1 \end{bmatrix} \begin{bmatrix} 1 & -a_1 \\ 0 & 1 \end{bmatrix}$$

$$= \begin{bmatrix} 1 - \underline{t}'a_2 & -(a_1 + a_2 - \underline{t}'a_1a_2) \\ \underline{t}' & 1 - \underline{t}'a_1 \end{bmatrix}$$

We describe the color aberration of this system by

$$\begin{bmatrix} db_{1,2} & -da_{1,2} \\ -dd_{1,2} & dc_{1,2} \end{bmatrix} = \begin{bmatrix} 0 & -da_2 \\ 0 & 0 \end{bmatrix} \begin{bmatrix} 1 & 0 \\ \underline{t}' & 1 \end{bmatrix} \begin{bmatrix} 1 & -a_1 \\ 0 & 1 \end{bmatrix}$$

$$+ \begin{bmatrix} 1 & -a_2 \\ 0 & 1 \end{bmatrix} \begin{bmatrix} 0 & 0 \\ d\underline{t}' & 0 \end{bmatrix} \begin{bmatrix} 1 & -a_1 \\ 0 & 1 \end{bmatrix}$$

$$+ \begin{bmatrix} 1 & -a_2 \\ 0 & 1 \end{bmatrix} \begin{bmatrix} 1 & 0 \\ \underline{t}' & 1 \end{bmatrix} \begin{bmatrix} 0 & -da_1 \\ 0 & 0 \end{bmatrix}$$

which equals

$$\begin{bmatrix} -\underline{t}' \, da_2 & -da_2(1 - a_1\underline{t}') \\ 0 & 0 \end{bmatrix}$$

$$+ \begin{bmatrix} -a_2 \, d\underline{t}' & a_1 a_2 \, d\underline{t}' \\ d\underline{t}' & -a_1 \, d\underline{t}' \end{bmatrix}$$

$$+ \begin{bmatrix} 0 & -(1 - a_2\underline{t}') \, da_1 \\ 0 & -\underline{t}' \, da_1 \end{bmatrix}$$

Now we find

$$da_{1,2} = (1 - a_2\underline{t}') \, da_1 + (1 - a_1\underline{t}') \, da_2 - a_1 a_2 \, d\underline{t}'$$
$$db_{1,2} = -a_2 \, d\underline{t}' - \underline{t}' \, da_2 \qquad\qquad\qquad (7\text{-}17)$$
$$dc_{1,2} = -a_1 \, d\underline{t}' - \underline{t}' \, da_1$$
$$dd_{1,2} = -d\underline{t}'$$

We know that

$$\nu = \frac{\mu_d - 1}{\mu_F - \mu_C} = \frac{\mu_d - 1}{d\mu} \qquad \text{or} \qquad d\mu = \frac{\mu_d - 1}{\nu} \qquad (7\text{-}18)$$

and

$$a_1 = \frac{\mu - 1}{r_1} \qquad \text{thus} \qquad da_1 = \frac{d\mu}{r_1} = \frac{\mu_d - 1}{\nu r_1} = \frac{a_1}{\nu} \qquad (7\text{-}19)$$

$$a_2 = \frac{1 - \mu}{r_2} \quad \text{thus} \quad da_2 = -\frac{d\mu}{r_2} = -\frac{\mu_d - 1}{\nu r_2} = \frac{a_2}{\nu} \qquad (7\text{-}20)$$

$$d\underline{t} = -\underline{t}' \frac{d\mu}{\mu} \qquad (7\text{-}21)$$

From this we find

$$da_{1,2} = (1 - a_2\underline{t}')\frac{a_1}{\nu} + a_1 a_2 \underline{t}' \frac{d\mu}{\mu} + (1 - a_1\underline{t}')\frac{a_2}{\nu}$$

$$= \frac{a_1 + a_2 - \underline{t}' a_1 a_2}{\nu} + a_1 a_2 \underline{t}'\left(\frac{d\mu}{\mu} - \frac{1}{\nu}\right)$$

$$= \frac{a_{1,2}}{\nu} + \frac{a_1 a_2 \underline{t}'}{\nu}\left(\frac{\mu_d - 1}{\mu_d} - 1\right)$$

$$= \frac{a_{1,2}}{\nu} - \frac{a_1 a_2 \underline{t}'}{\mu_d} \qquad (7\text{-}22)$$

$$db_{1,2} = +a_2\underline{t}' \frac{d\mu}{\mu_d} - \underline{t}' \frac{a_2}{\nu} = a_2\underline{t}'\left(\frac{d\mu}{\mu_d} - \frac{1}{\nu}\right) = -\frac{a_2 \underline{t}'}{\mu_d \nu} \qquad (7\text{-}23)$$

$$dc_{1,2} = -\frac{a_1 \underline{t}'}{\mu_d \nu} \qquad (7\text{-}24)$$

$$dd_{1,2} = \frac{\underline{t}'(\mu_d - 1)}{\mu_d} \qquad (7\text{-}25)$$

It is impossible to make all these quantities zero at the same time.

Thin Systems

A thin system is one in which two or more thin lenses are combined in such a way that all the $\underline{t}'$ values are equal to zero. A system of e thin lenses can be described thus

$$\begin{bmatrix} b_{1,e} & -a_{1,e} \\ -d_{1,e} & c_{1,e} \end{bmatrix} = \begin{bmatrix} 1 & -a_e \\ 0 & 1 \end{bmatrix} \begin{bmatrix} 1 & -a_{e-1} \\ 0 & 1 \end{bmatrix} \cdots \begin{bmatrix} 1 & -a_n \\ 0 & 1 \end{bmatrix}$$

$$\cdots \begin{bmatrix} 1 & -a_2 \\ 0 & 1 \end{bmatrix} \begin{bmatrix} 1 & -a_1 \\ 0 & 1 \end{bmatrix}$$

$$= \begin{bmatrix} 1 & -a_e \\ 0 & 1 \end{bmatrix} \begin{bmatrix} 1 & -a_{e-1} \\ 0 & 1 \end{bmatrix} \cdots \begin{bmatrix} 1 & -a_n \\ 0 & 1 \end{bmatrix}$$

$$\cdots \begin{bmatrix} 1 & -(a_1 + a_2) \\ 0 & 1 \end{bmatrix}$$

$$= \begin{bmatrix} 1 & -a_e \\ 0 & 1 \end{bmatrix} \begin{bmatrix} 1 & -a_{e-1} \\ 0 & 1 \end{bmatrix}$$

$$\cdots \begin{bmatrix} 1 & -(a_n + \cdots + a_2 + a_1) \\ 0 & 1 \end{bmatrix}$$

$$= \begin{bmatrix} 1 & -\sum\limits_{n=1}^{e} a_n \\ 0 & 1 \end{bmatrix} \tag{7-26}$$

Multiplying these matrices simply amounts to the addition of the powers of the individual components. The color aberrations of this system can be written

$$\begin{bmatrix} db & -da \\ -dd & dc \end{bmatrix} = \begin{bmatrix} 1 & -a_e \\ 0 & 1 \end{bmatrix} \cdots \begin{bmatrix} 1 & -a_2 \\ 0 & 1 \end{bmatrix} \begin{bmatrix} 0 & -da_1 \\ 0 & 0 \end{bmatrix} + \begin{bmatrix} 1 & -a_e \\ 0 & 1 \end{bmatrix}$$

$$\cdots \begin{bmatrix} 1 & -a_{n+1} \\ 0 & 1 \end{bmatrix} \begin{bmatrix} 0 & -da_n \\ 0 & 0 \end{bmatrix} \begin{bmatrix} 1 & -a_{n-1} \\ 0 & 1 \end{bmatrix}$$

$$\cdots \begin{bmatrix} 1 & a_1 \\ 0 & 1 \end{bmatrix}$$

$$+ \begin{bmatrix} 0 & -da_e \\ 0 & 0 \end{bmatrix} \begin{bmatrix} 1 & -a_{e-1} \\ 0 & 1 \end{bmatrix} \cdots \begin{bmatrix} 1 & -a_1 \\ 0 & 1 \end{bmatrix}$$

Or, in general, this can be written as follows

$$\begin{bmatrix} db & -da \\ -dd & dc \end{bmatrix} = \sum_{n=1}^{e} \begin{bmatrix} 1 & -a_e \\ 0 & 1 \end{bmatrix} \cdots \begin{bmatrix} 1 & -a_{n+1} \\ 0 & 1 \end{bmatrix} \begin{bmatrix} 0 & -da_n \\ 0 & 0 \end{bmatrix} \begin{bmatrix} 1 & -a_{n-1} \\ 0 & 1 \end{bmatrix}$$

$$\cdots \begin{bmatrix} 1 & -a_1 \\ 0 & 1 \end{bmatrix}$$

$$= \sum_{n=1}^{e} \begin{bmatrix} 1 & -\sum\limits_{m=e}^{n+1} a_n \\ 0 & 1 \end{bmatrix} \begin{bmatrix} 0 & -da_n \\ 0 & 0 \end{bmatrix} \begin{bmatrix} 1 & -\sum\limits_{p=n-1}^{1} a_p \\ 0 & 1 \end{bmatrix}$$

$$= \sum_{n=1}^{e} \begin{bmatrix} 1 & -\sum\limits_{m=e}^{n+1} a_m \\ 0 & 0 \end{bmatrix} = \begin{bmatrix} 0 & -da_n \\ 0 & 0 \end{bmatrix}$$

$$= \sum_{n=1}^{e} \begin{bmatrix} 0 & -da_n \\ 0 & 0 \end{bmatrix} = \begin{bmatrix} 0 & -\sum\limits_{n=1}^{e} da_n \\ 0 & 0 \end{bmatrix} \qquad (7\text{-}27)$$

Thus we get

$$da = \sum_{n=1}^{e} da_n = \sum_{n=1}^{e} \frac{a_n}{\nu n} \qquad (7\text{-}28)$$

and

$$db = dc = dd = 0 \qquad (7\text{-}29)$$

This gives us a way to work with ν values which cannot be ob-tained directly from the glass tables. If we say

$$da = \frac{a}{\nu} = \sum_{n=1}^{e} \frac{a_n}{\nu n} \qquad (7\text{-}30)$$

we can make any ν value we need by combining thin lenses.

Let us now try to set up a color-corrected thin system having a positive power and consisting of two thin lenses.

We know that

$$db = dc = dd = 0$$

$$da = \frac{a_1}{\nu_1} + \frac{a_2}{\nu_2}$$

We can make da = 0.
We want a system with a positive power so

$$a = a_1 + a_2$$

and

$$a_2 = a - a_1$$

Now

$$\frac{a_1}{\nu_1} + \frac{a - a_1}{\nu_2} = 0$$

$$a_1 \left(\frac{1}{\nu_1} - \frac{1}{\nu_2} \right) = - \frac{a}{\nu_2} \qquad (7\text{-}31)$$

$$a_1 = \frac{a\nu_1}{\nu_1 - \nu_2}$$

Also

$$\frac{a}{\nu_1 - \nu_2} = - \frac{a_2}{\nu_2} \qquad (7\text{-}32)$$

From this we see that the power of each component has the opposite sign. Furthermore the component with the larger ν value has the same sign as the power of the total lens system. The smaller the difference in ν values, the greater the power of the individual components becomes. To find the over-all power of the doublet we simply add the powers of its components.

As an example let us take a real lens with these characteristics.

$$a = +1$$

$$\nu_1 = 60 \text{ (crown glass)}$$

$$\nu_2 = 30 \text{ (flint glass)}$$

We know that

$$a_1 = \frac{1 \times 60}{60 - 30} = +2$$

$$a_2 = -\frac{1 \times 30}{60 - 30} = -1$$

So we have a two-element lens that is color corrected and has a power of +1.

We see that color correction is dependent on the power of the components and not on their shape.

A color-corrected lens is actually corrected for only two wavelengths. What happens to the focal length for the other wavelengths is shown in Fig. 7-3, curve b. In Fig. 7-3 the line a shows the change in focal length of a simple lens.

Other Systems

Let us now see whether or not we can achieve a color correction with two thin lenses separated by a distance t. The normal matrix for this system is

$$\begin{bmatrix} 1 - a_2t & -(a_1 + a_2 - ta_1a_2) \\ t & 1 - a_1t \end{bmatrix}$$

$dt = 0$ because the space between the lenses is air.
The matrix for color aberration is

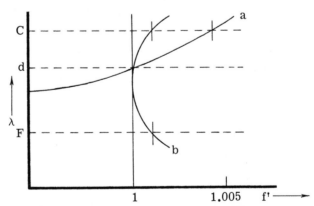

Fig. 7-3.   Color correction of lenses.

$$\begin{bmatrix} 1 & -a_2 \\ 0 & 1 \end{bmatrix} \begin{bmatrix} 1 & 0 \\ t & 1 \end{bmatrix} \begin{bmatrix} 0 & -\dfrac{a_1}{\nu_1} \\ 0 & 0 \end{bmatrix}$$

$$+ \begin{bmatrix} 0 & -\dfrac{a_2}{\nu_2} \\ 0 & 0 \end{bmatrix} \begin{bmatrix} 1 & 0 \\ t & 1 \end{bmatrix} \begin{bmatrix} 1 & -a_1 \\ 0 & 1 \end{bmatrix}$$

$$= \begin{bmatrix} 0 & -\dfrac{a_1}{\nu_1} + \dfrac{a_1 a_2}{\nu_1} t \\ 0 & \dfrac{a_1}{\nu_1} t \end{bmatrix} + \begin{bmatrix} -\dfrac{a_2 t}{\nu_2} & -\dfrac{a_2}{\nu_2}(1 - a_1 t) \\ 0 & 0 \end{bmatrix}$$

From this we find

$$da = \frac{a_1}{\nu_1} - \frac{a_1}{\nu_1} a_2 t + \frac{a_2}{\nu_2}(1 - a_1 t)$$

$$db = -\frac{a_2}{\nu_2} t$$

$$dc = -\frac{a_1}{\nu_1} t \qquad\qquad\qquad (7\text{-}33)$$

$$dd = 0$$

Again we see that under most conditions we cannot correct for color aberrations with two single air-spaced lenses. However, let us look into the following case:

$$a = a_1 + a_2 - t a_1 a_2 \qquad\qquad\qquad (7\text{-}34)$$

$$0 = \frac{a_1}{\nu_1}(1 - a_2 t) + \frac{a_2}{\nu_2}(1 - a_1 t) \qquad\qquad (7\text{-}35)$$

or

$$\frac{a_1}{\nu_1} + \frac{a_2}{\nu_2} - a_1 a_2 t\left(\frac{1}{\nu_1} + \frac{1}{\nu_2}\right) = 0$$

from which we determine

$$t = \frac{\dfrac{a_1}{\nu_1} + \dfrac{a_2}{\nu_2}}{a_1 a_2 \left(\dfrac{1}{\nu_1} + \dfrac{1}{\nu_2}\right)} = \frac{a_1 \nu_2 + a_2 \nu_1}{a_1 a_2 (\nu_2 + \nu_1)} \qquad\qquad (7\text{-}36)$$

Assuming that the total power of the system is equal to $+1$, Eq. (7-34) becomes

$$a_1 + a_2 - ta_1a_2 = 1$$

Using Eq. (7-36) to eliminate t, we find

$$a_1 + a_2 - \frac{a_1\nu_2 + a_2\nu_1}{\nu_2 + \nu_1} = 1$$

or   (7-37)

$$\frac{a_1\nu_1 + a_2\nu_2}{\nu_2 + \nu_1} = 1$$

If both lenses are now made of the same glass, or

$$\nu_1 = \nu_2$$

then Eq. (7-37) becomes

$$\frac{a_1 + a_2}{2} = 1$$

and Eq. (7-36) becomes

$$t = \frac{a_1 + a_2}{2a_1a_2} = \frac{1}{a_1a_2}$$

This, then, is the solution wherein we have corrected the power of the lenses without correcting the positions of the unit surfaces and the focal points.

By using the same glass for both lenses we have corrected the power not only for two wavelengths but actually for all the wavelengths.

The ordinary eyepieces of microscopes and telescopes are achromatized according to this principle.

If f_1' is a few times f_2' we have a so-called Huygens eyepiece. If f_1' is equal to f_2' we have a Ramsden eyepiece (Fig. 7-4). Usually the distance between the lenses in a Ramsden eyepiece is a little smaller than required for achromatism, because one wants the object focal point outside the lens and not in the first lens where it would come if the above formula were used. If it were in the first lens it

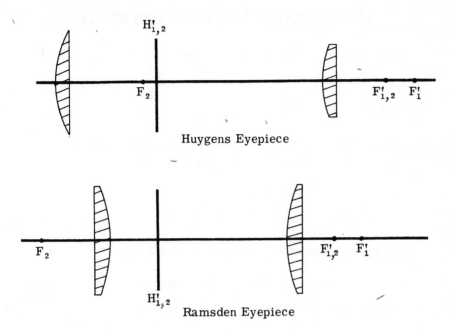

$H'_{1,2}$

F_2

$F'_{1,2}$ F'_1

Huygens Eyepiece

F_2

$F'_{1,2}$ F'_1

$H'_{1,2}$

Ramsden Eyepiece

Fig. 7-4. Examples of eyepieces.

would also image all the scratches and dirt on this lens.

More information on this subject can be found in References 6, 15, 20, 21, 22, 43, 47, and 60.

MATRIX DESCRIPTION OF DIFFERENTIALS

If we have the following set of equations

$$\begin{bmatrix} x' \\ y' \end{bmatrix} = \begin{bmatrix} a & b \\ c & e \end{bmatrix} \begin{bmatrix} x \\ y \end{bmatrix}$$

the values of a, b, c and e could be changed by a small value to a + da, b + db, c + dc, and e + de. We then have

$$\begin{bmatrix} x' + dx' \\ y' + dy' \end{bmatrix} = \begin{bmatrix} a + da & b + db \\ c + dc & e + de \end{bmatrix} \begin{bmatrix} x \\ y \end{bmatrix}$$

We can introduce the addition of matrices and write

$$\begin{bmatrix} x' \\ y' \end{bmatrix} + \begin{bmatrix} dx' \\ dy' \end{bmatrix} = \begin{bmatrix} a & b \\ c & e \end{bmatrix} \begin{bmatrix} x \\ y \end{bmatrix} + \begin{bmatrix} da & db \\ dc & de \end{bmatrix} \begin{bmatrix} x \\ y \end{bmatrix} \qquad (7\text{-}11)$$

or

$$\begin{bmatrix} dx' \\ dy' \end{bmatrix} = \begin{bmatrix} da & db \\ dc & de \end{bmatrix} \begin{bmatrix} x \\ y \end{bmatrix} \qquad (7\text{-}12)$$

It is now clear that we can write in general

$$\begin{bmatrix} x' \\ y' \end{bmatrix} = M_e \cdots M_{n+1} \cdot M_n \cdot M_{n-1} \cdots M_2 M_1 \begin{bmatrix} x \\ y \end{bmatrix}$$

If we denote a matrix of the form above as dM_n we then have

$$\begin{bmatrix} x' + dx' \\ y' + dy' \end{bmatrix} = (M_e + dM_e) \cdots (M_{n+1} + dM_{n+1})(M_n + dM_n)$$

$$(M_{n-1} + dM_{n-1}) \cdots (M_2 + dM_2) (M_1 + dM_1) \begin{bmatrix} x \\ y \end{bmatrix}$$

Now we can neglect all the quadratic terms in differentials, thus $dM_a \cdot dM_b = 0$.
Thus we find

$$\begin{bmatrix} dx' \\ dy' \end{bmatrix} \begin{bmatrix} (dM_e)M_{e+1,1} + \ldots + M_{e,n+2}(dM_{n+1})M_{n,1} + \\ \ldots + M_{e,n+1}(dM_n M_{n-1,1} + M_{e,n}(dM_{n-1})M_{n-2,1} + \\ \ldots + M_{e,3}\, dM_2 M_1 + M_{e,2}\, dM_1 \end{bmatrix} \begin{bmatrix} x \\ y \end{bmatrix}$$

or

$$\begin{bmatrix} dx' \\ dy' \end{bmatrix} = \begin{bmatrix} \sum_1^0 nM_{e,n+1}\, dM_n\, M_{n-1,1} \end{bmatrix} \begin{bmatrix} x \\ y \end{bmatrix} \tag{7-13}$$

Example:

If a matrix with its differential is given by

$$M + dM \begin{bmatrix} a & b \\ c & e \end{bmatrix} + \begin{bmatrix} da & db \\ dc & de \end{bmatrix}$$

we can then ask what dM is for the whole system if

$$M = \begin{bmatrix} a_4 & b_4 \\ c_4 & e_4 \end{bmatrix} \begin{bmatrix} a_3 & b_3 \\ c_3 & e_3 \end{bmatrix} \begin{bmatrix} a_2 & b_2 \\ c_2 & e_2 \end{bmatrix} \begin{bmatrix} a_1 & b_1 \\ c_1 & e_1 \end{bmatrix}$$

Now

$$\begin{aligned}
dM = &\begin{bmatrix} da_4 & db_4 \\ dc_4 & de_4 \end{bmatrix} \begin{bmatrix} a_3 & b_3 \\ c_3 & e_3 \end{bmatrix} \begin{bmatrix} a_2 & b_2 \\ c_2 & e_2 \end{bmatrix} \begin{bmatrix} a_1 & b_1 \\ c_1 & e_1 \end{bmatrix} \\
+ &\begin{bmatrix} a_4 & b_4 \\ c_4 & e_4 \end{bmatrix} \begin{bmatrix} da_3 & db_3 \\ dc_3 & de_3 \end{bmatrix} \begin{bmatrix} a_2 & b_2 \\ c_2 & e_2 \end{bmatrix} \begin{bmatrix} a_1 & b_1 \\ c_1 & e_1 \end{bmatrix} \\
+ &\begin{bmatrix} a_4 & b_4 \\ c_4 & e_4 \end{bmatrix} \begin{bmatrix} a_3 & b_3 \\ c_3 & e_3 \end{bmatrix} \begin{bmatrix} da_2 & db_2 \\ dc_2 & de_2 \end{bmatrix} \begin{bmatrix} a_1 & b_1 \\ c_1 & e_1 \end{bmatrix} \\
+ &\begin{bmatrix} a_4 & b_4 \\ c_4 & e_4 \end{bmatrix} \begin{bmatrix} a_3 & b_3 \\ c_3 & e_3 \end{bmatrix} \begin{bmatrix} a_2 & b_2 \\ c_2 & e_2 \end{bmatrix} \begin{bmatrix} da_1 & db_1 \\ dc_1 & de_1 \end{bmatrix}
\end{aligned}$$

Chapter 8

THIRD-ORDER ABBERATIONS

Until now we have been describing optics with only the ray concept.

Although this concept is perfectly adequate for describing third-order aberrations, we shall start our description of the third-order aberrations from a different viewpoint, i. e., from the description of a wavefront with aberrations. There are several reasons for doing this. A great deal of lens testing is done with some kind of interferometer and the understanding of this technique requires a knowledge of waveforms. If diffraction is taken into account when calculating the light distribution in the image of a point object, we have to start with the wavefront. In addition, in calculating the sine wave transfer function the wavefront is the proper starting point. It is easier to go from the wavefront description to the ray description than vice versa; therefore, we shall start this description from the wavefront.

A point P in the object space (Fig. 8-1) in the ray description emits rays in all directions. They all come from the point P. In the wavefront description such a point P emits spherical waves. (A wavefront is a surface where the waves all have the same phase.) The definition of a lightray can also be given as the lines perpendicular to the wavefronts. Because of this fact one can describe the image by giving the position of all the rays forming the image, or, equally sufficient, describing a wavefront which will form this image. Either one gives a complete description.

If we want to describe a wavefront in the image space of a lens system we can select any reference plane. It is usual, although not necessary, to choose the exit pupil.

Suppose that point P' (x_p', y_p') is the paraxial image point of P (Fig. 8-2). Suppose the plane $x_1'Qy_1'$ is the exit pupil (or any other

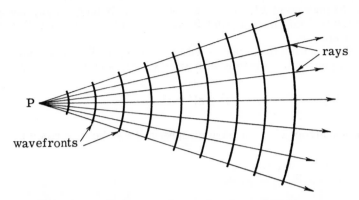

Fig. 8-1.   Relation of wavefronts and lightrays.

reference plane). If the optical system under consideration were perfect the emerging wavefront would be a sphere with point P' as the center. This is easily seen by remembering that the lightrays are perpendicular to the wavefront. All the lines perpendicular to a sphere go through the center of the sphere, or all the rays go ex-

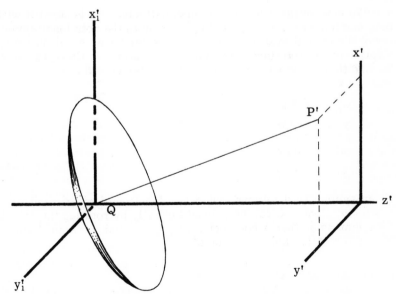

Fig. 8-2.   Coordinates used in describing a wavefront.

actly through point P'. If we do not have a perfect image, not all
the rays will go through point P' and thus the wavefront will deviate
from a sphere.

The equation of a sphere with its center in P' and a radius P'Q
= r in a coordinate system with axes x', y', and z' is denoted by

$$(x_1' - x')^2 + (y_1' - y')^2 + z_1'^2 = r^2 \tag{8-1}$$

If the wavefront is not a perfect sphere it can be described by

$$(x_1' - x_p')^2 + (y_1' - y_p')^2 + z_1'^2 = (r + \Delta)^2 \tag{8-2}$$

where x_p' and y_p' are the coordinates of the paraxial image point and
Δ the wavefront deviation. Now we can write this as

$$(x_1' - x_p')^2 + (y_1' - y_p')^2 + z_1'^2 = r^2 + 2r\Delta + \Delta^2$$

If the quantity Δ is small compared to r we may neglect Δ^2. Thus
we find

$$(x_1' - x_p')^2 + (y_1' - y_p')^2 + z_1'^2 - r^2 - 2r\Delta = 0 \tag{8-3}$$

We now investigate what form Δ will have. In general it will
be a function of x', y', x_1', and y_1'. Owing to the rotational symmetry of the optical systems we shall consider here, Δ will be only a
function of the rotational invariant combinations of these variables.
To find these it is easier to convert to polar coordinates

$$\begin{aligned} x_p' &= \rho \sin \alpha \\ y_p' &= \rho \cos \alpha \end{aligned} \tag{8-4}$$

$$\begin{aligned} x_1' &= r_1 \sin \phi \\ y_1' &= r_1 \cos \phi \end{aligned} \tag{8-5}$$

From symmetry it follows that Δ is a function of r_1^2, ρ^2, and $r_1\rho$
$\cos(\phi - \alpha)$ alone. It can be proved formally by rotating the axis and
then demanding that Δ does not change magnitude or sign. This
means that Δ is also a function of

$$2u_1' = x_p'^2 + y_p'^2 = \rho^2 \tag{8-6}$$

$$\begin{aligned} u_2' &= x_p'x_1' + y_p'y_1' = r_1\rho \,(\sin \phi \sin \alpha + \cos \phi \cos \alpha) \\ &= r_1\rho \,\cos(\phi - \alpha) \end{aligned} \tag{8-7}$$

$$2u_3' = x_1'^2 + y_1'^2 = r_1^2 \qquad (8-8)$$

Δ will be of a very complicated form. For this reason we shall develop it into a power series. By discontinuing the series after the quadratic terms in u this power series will, in general, have the form

$$\Delta = a_0 + b_0 u_1' + b_1 u_2' + b_2 u_3' + \frac{1}{2}c_0 u_1'^2 + c_1 u_1' u_2' + c_2 u_1' u_3'$$

$$+ \frac{1}{2}c_3 u_2'^2 + c_4 u_2' u_3' + \frac{1}{2}c_5 u_3'^2 + \ldots \qquad (8-9)$$

The coefficients a_i, b_i, and c_i determine the form of the wavefront and are different for different optical systems.

If we introduce Eq. (8-9) in (8-3) we have the complete equation for the wavefront.

To find the lightrays we have to find the normals to this wavefront. In general, if the equation of a surface is given by $f(x_1',y_1',z_1')$ the normal in a point x_1', y_1', z_1' is given by

$$\frac{x_1' - x'}{\dfrac{\delta f}{\delta x_1'}} = \frac{y_1' - y'}{\dfrac{\delta f}{\delta y_1'}} = \frac{z_1' - z'}{\dfrac{\delta f}{\delta z_1'}}$$

where x', y', and z' are the coordinates of any point on this line. Applying this formula to the equation for the wavefront (Eq. 8-3)

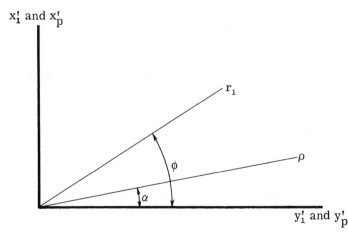

Fig. 8-3. Polar coordinates in exit pupil and image plane.

we find for the equation of the lightrays

$$\frac{x_i' - x'}{2(x_i' - x_p') - 2r\frac{\delta\Delta}{\delta x_i'}} = \frac{y_i' - y'}{2(y_i' - y_p') - 2r\frac{\delta\Delta}{\delta y_i'}} = \frac{z_i' - z'}{2z_i'}$$

or

$$x_i' - x' = \left(1 - \frac{z'}{z_i'}\right)\left\{x_i' - x_p' - r\frac{\delta\Delta}{\delta x_i'}\right\} \tag{8-10}$$

$$y_i' - y' = \left(1 - \frac{z'}{z_i'}\right)\left\{y_i' - y_p' - r\frac{\delta\Delta}{\delta y_i'}\right\} \tag{8-11}$$

or

$$x' = x_p' + r\frac{\delta\Delta}{\delta x_i'} + \frac{z'}{z_i'}x_i' - \frac{z'}{z_i'}x_p' - \frac{z'}{z_i'}r\frac{\delta\Delta}{\delta x_i'}$$

$$y' = y_p' + r\frac{\delta\Delta}{\delta y_i'} + \frac{z'}{z_i'}y_i' - \frac{z'}{z_i'}y_p' - \frac{z'}{z_i'}r\frac{\delta\Delta}{\delta y_i'}$$

When only the quadratic terms of the series for Δ are taken into account, our formulation is only valid if x_p', y_p', $\delta\Delta/\delta x'$, and $\delta\Delta/\delta y'$ are small. We shall use these formulas to investigate the immediate neighborhood of our paraxial image point. Thus, z' is small and we will, therefore, neglect all the quantities where a product of two small quantities appears. The quantity z_i', in this region, will therefore always be approximately equal to r. So we find

$$x' = x_p' + z'\frac{x_i'}{r} + r\frac{\delta\Delta}{\delta x_i'}$$

$$y' = y_p' + z'\frac{y_i'}{r} + r\frac{\delta\Delta}{\delta y_i'} \tag{8-12}$$

We see that for the paraxial image plane ($z' = 0$) this reduces to

$$x' = x_p' + r\frac{\delta\Delta}{\delta x_i'}$$

$$y' = y_p' + r\frac{\delta\Delta}{\delta y_i'} \tag{8-13}$$

Now for a perfect spherical wavefront we have $\Delta = 0$ and thus we find from Eq. (8-12) for the paraxial ray intercepts in this case

$$x' = x'_p + z'\frac{x'_i}{r}$$

$$y' = y'_p + z'\frac{y'_i}{r} \tag{8-14}$$

By introducing Eq. (8-9) into (8-13) we will have found x' and y', including the third-order aberration terms. We have

$$\frac{\delta u'_1}{\delta x'_i} = 0 \qquad \frac{\delta u'_1}{\delta y'_i} = 0$$

$$\frac{\delta u'_2}{\delta x'_i} = x'_p \qquad \frac{\delta u'_2}{\delta y'_i} = y'_p$$

$$\frac{\delta u'_3}{\delta x'_i} = x'_i \qquad \frac{\delta u'_3}{\delta y'_i} = y'_i$$

and thus find

$$\frac{\delta\Delta}{\delta x'_i} = b_1 x'_p + b_2 x'_i + c_1 u'_1 x'_p + c_2 u'_1 x'_i + c_3 u'_2 x'_i + c_4 u'_2 x'_i$$

$$+ c_4 u'_3 x'_p + c_5 u'_3 x'_i \tag{8-15}$$

$$\frac{\delta\Delta}{\delta y'_i} = b_1 y'_p + b_2 y'_i + c_1 u'_1 y'_p + c_2 u'_1 y'_i + c_3 u'_2 y'_i + c_4 u'_2 y'_i$$

$$+ c_4 u'_3 y'_p + c_5 u'_3 y'_i \tag{8-16}$$

Introducing Eq. (8-15) in (8-13) we find

$$x' = x'_p + r\{b_1 x'_p + b_2 x'_i + \ldots\} \tag{8-17}$$

We must remember that we introduced the equation for Δ in its most general form and b_1 and b_2 are thus coefficients which have to be determined.

In doing so we have to make Eq. (8-14) equal to (8-17) and thus

$$b_1 = 0 \quad \text{and} \quad b_2 = \frac{z'}{r^2} \tag{8-18}$$

It is customary to write the aberration equations with the variables x and y of the point P in the object and x_1 and y_1 in the entrance pupil (or the plane in the object space conjugated to the reference plane in the image space).

Paraxially we have

$$x'_p = \beta'x \qquad y'_p = \beta'y$$
$$x'_1 = \beta'_1 x_1 \qquad y'_1 = \beta'_1 y_1$$
(8-19)

If we introduce

$$rc_1\beta'^3 = C_{10}$$
$$rc_2\beta'^2\beta'_1 = C_{20}$$
$$rc_3\beta'^2\beta'_1 = C_{11}$$
$$rc_4\beta'\beta'^2_1 = C_{21} = C_{12}$$
$$rc_5\beta'^3_1 = C_{22}$$
(8-20)

and

$$u'_1 = \beta'^2 u_1$$
$$u'_2 = \beta'\beta'_1 u_2$$
$$u'_3 = \beta'^2_1 u_3$$
(8-21)

we find in the paraxial image plane

$$x' = \beta'x + C_{10}u_1x + C_{20}u_1x_1 + C_{11}u_2x + C_{21}u_2x_1$$
$$+ C_{12}u_3x + C_{22}u_3x_1$$
(8-22)

$$y' = \beta'y + C_{10}u_1y + C_{20}u_1y_1 + C_{11}u_2y + C_{21}u_2y_1$$
$$+ C_{12}u_3y + C_{22}u_3y_1$$
(8-23)

where

$$C_{21} = C_{12}$$

For a given system we shall have to determine the values of the $C_{i,j}$. This we shall do later, but first we shall investigate what it means when these coefficients have certain values.

We shall include in this investigation the wavefront aberrations, measured with an interferometer, the spread of the rays in the image plane (blur circle), and the shadow of a single wire placed in the vicinity of the image point since this is easily related to the Ronchi test.

In Eqs. (8-9), (8-22) and (8-23) we can investigate the role of each coefficient by assuming that all the others are equal to 0.

SPHERICAL ABERRATION $C_{22} \neq 0$ or $c_5 \neq 0$

Introducing the above condition into Eqs. (8-22) and (8-23), including the defocusing terms (8-14), we find

$$
\begin{aligned}
x' &= \beta'x + \beta_1'\frac{z'}{r}x_1 + C_{22}u_3x_1 \\
y' &= \beta'y + \beta_1'\frac{z'}{r}y_1 + C_{22}u_3y_1
\end{aligned}
\tag{8-24}
$$

Now u_3 is a function of x_1 and y_1. This means that this is the only aberration which exists on axis where $x = 0$ and $y = 0$ because each of the other terms of Eqs. (8-22) and (8-23) contains at least one factor, x or y. We also see that this aberration is independent of x and y and thus, when it exists, exists over the whole field. The terms $\beta'x$ and $\beta'y$ merely move the paraxial image out into the proper point in the image plane while the terms $C_{22}u_3x_1$ and $C_{22}u_3y_1$ describe the aberrations of the rays around this paraxial image point.

To begin, let us examine this aberration in the paraxial image plane ($z' = 0$). We now have

$$
\begin{aligned}
x' - \beta'x' &= C_{22}u_3x_1 = \frac{1}{2}C_{22}(x_1^2 + y_1^2)x_1 \\
y' - \beta'y' &= C_{22}u_3y_1 = \frac{1}{2}C_{22}(x_1^2 + y_1^2)y_1
\end{aligned}
\tag{8-25}
$$

If we again introduce polar coordinates we have

$$
\begin{aligned}
\Delta x' &= \frac{1}{2}C_{22}r_1^3 \sin \phi \\
\Delta y' &= \frac{1}{2}C_{22}r_1^3 \cos \phi
\end{aligned}
$$

or, squaring and adding

$$
\Delta x'^2 + \Delta y'^2 = \left(\frac{1}{2}C_{22}r_1^3\right)^2
$$

This is a circle with the paraxial image point as its center, with a radius $1/2C_{22}r_1^3$. The size will be determined by the radius r_1 of the ring in the entrance pupil through which the ray passes.

The spread of the rays in the image point for a lens with a circular aperture will be a circular disc of light whose size is determined by the magnitude of C_{22} and the third power of the maximum radius in the entrance pupil. This maximum radius in the image disc is called the transverse spherical aberration (TA) and is given by

$$TA = \frac{1}{2} C_{22}r_{1_m}^3 \tag{8-26}$$

where r_{1_m} is the radius of the edge of the entrance pupil (Fig. 8-4).

If we introduce the defocusing term again we have Eq. (8-24). We can now ask where the ray, going through the edge of the entrance pupil, meets the axis $(x' = 0)$. Owing to the symmetry we can take, without loss of generality, the ray for which $y_1 = 0$ and thus $x_1 = r_1$, and we find

$$0 = \beta_1' \frac{z_m'}{r} r_{1_m} + \frac{1}{2}C_{22}r_{1_m}^3 \tag{8-27}$$

$$z_m' = -\frac{C_{22}r_{1_m}^2 r}{2\beta_1'}$$

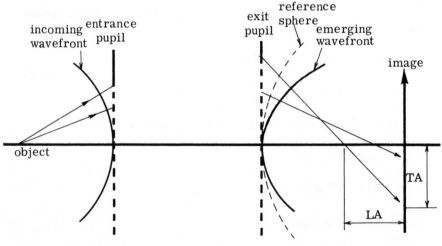

Fig. 8-4. Wavefronts passing a system with spherical aberration.

This distance z'_m is called longitudinal spherical aberration (LA).
The equation for the deviation of the wavefront is given by

$$\Delta = \frac{z'}{r^2}u'_3 + \frac{1}{2}c_5u'^2_3 \qquad (8\text{-}28)$$

If we take the paraxial image point as the center of our reference sphere ($z' = 0$) we have

$$\Delta = \frac{1}{2}c_5u'^2_3 = \frac{1}{8}c_5r'^4_1 \qquad (8\text{-}29)$$

This is a parabola. If we defocus we find

$$\Delta = \frac{z'}{r^2}u'_3 + \frac{1}{2}c_5u'^2_3 = \frac{1}{2}\frac{z'}{r^2}r'^2_1 + \frac{1}{8}c_5r'^4_1 \qquad (8\text{-}30)$$

This we can use to minimize the effect of spherical aberration, if we choose a point on axis such that the Δ is 0 at the edge of the aperture. This gives us

$$0 = \frac{1}{2}\frac{z'}{r^2}r'^2_{1m} + \frac{1}{8}c_5r'^4_{1m}$$

$$z' = -\frac{1}{4}c_5r'^2_{1m}r^2 \qquad (8\text{-}31)$$

Or, with the help of Eqs. (8-20) and (8-27)

$$z' = -\frac{C_{22}r'^2_{1m}r}{4\beta'^3_1} = -\frac{C_{22}r^2_{1m}r}{4\beta'_1} = \frac{1}{2}z'_m \qquad (8\text{-}32)$$

This shows that by focusing halfway between the paraxial and marginal image point (z'_m) we have a minimum of aberration spread in the image. The shape of the wavefronts for the various positions of the image plane are shown in Fig. 8-5. The above situation represents the smallest deviation from a spherical wavefront.

If we place our object point on axis and place a wire close to the image in the bundle we can ask which rays are intercepted by this wire. We can experimentally investigate this by placing the eye close behind the wire and looking toward the exit pupil. The

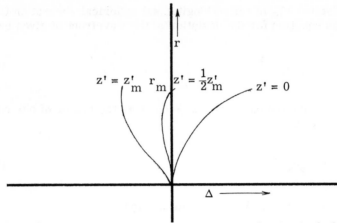

Fig. 8-5. Influencing of focusing in presence of spherical aberration.

rays intercepted by the wire will cause us to see dark areas in the exit pupil. Another way of making these areas visible is to place a screen (or photographic film) a certain distance behind the image point. If there were no wire we would see an illuminated circle. The rays intercepted by the wire will show up as shadows of the same form as seen by the eye in the exit pupil. This is easily comprehended if we realize that the aberrations are small (the distance of the screen is large, just as r was large, compared to the aberration) and thus for all practical purposes we have a perfect projection from the exit pupil on the screen. The distance between the paraxial image and screen and the distance r determines the size of the shadow on the screen. For simplicity we assume in the following that both distances are equal and the equation of the shadow in the exit pupil is the same as the one on the screen.

Now if we place the wire parallel to the y' axis, a distance of x_0' away from it, and a distance $z_0'r/\beta_1'$ from the paraxial image plane we will have all the rays going through this line intercepted. So all these rays are given by making $x' = x_0'$ and $z' = z_0'r/\beta_1'$ in Eq. (8-24). This gives

$$x_0' = z_0'x_1 + C_{22}(x_1^2 + y_1^2)x_1 = x_1\{z_0' + C_{22}(x_1^2 + y_1^2)\} \qquad (8-33)$$

It is easily seen that this is the equation of the dark areas in the exit pupil if we consider x_1 and y_1 as the variables. This is only true if the magnification of the pupils is $+1$. In all other cases we shall have to introduce $x_1' = \beta_1'x_1$ and $y_1' = \beta_1'y_1$. In order to keep the formulas simple we shall omit this and assume $\beta_1' = +1$.

Let us first consider the case where the wire intersects the axis or $x_0' = 0$. We now have the equation

$$0 = x_1 \left\{ z_0' + C_{22}(x_1'^2 + y_1'^2) \right\} \tag{8-34}$$

or

$$x_1 = 0$$

and

$$-\frac{z_0'}{C_{22}} = x_1^2 + y_1^2 \tag{8-35}$$

The first equation is a straight line, going through the center parallel to the wire. This part is clear from symmetry. The second equation is a circle if the sign of z_0 is opposite to that of C_{22}. Where z_0 and C_{22} have the same sign the equation is imaginary and the shadow reduces to the above straight line. The circle is easily understood by the fact that a certain circular zone in the exit pupil will focus in one point on the axis and thus will be totally intersected by the wire. If we increase z_0 we shall have a shadow which gets larger and larger until $z_0' r / \beta_1' = z_m'$ and the ring gets out of the illuminated area. Where x_0' is not zero the equation represents a curve of one of the forms shown in Fig. 8-6.

By measuring x_0', z_0', β_1', r, and the form of the curve (easiest if $x_0' = 0$ and measuring the radius of the shadow) we can easily calculate the value of C_{22}.

COMA $C_{12} \neq C_{21} \neq 0$ and $c_4 \neq 0$

In this case it is unimportant to include defocusing. So in the paraxial image plane we have

$$x' = \beta' x + C_{12}(u_2 x_1 + u_3 x)$$
$$y' = \beta' y + C_{12}(u_2 y_1 + u_3 y) \tag{8-36}$$

Owing to the symmetry it is immaterial which object point at a distance ρ from the axis is selected. They will each give the same pattern in the image plane. Thus we can investigate the point on

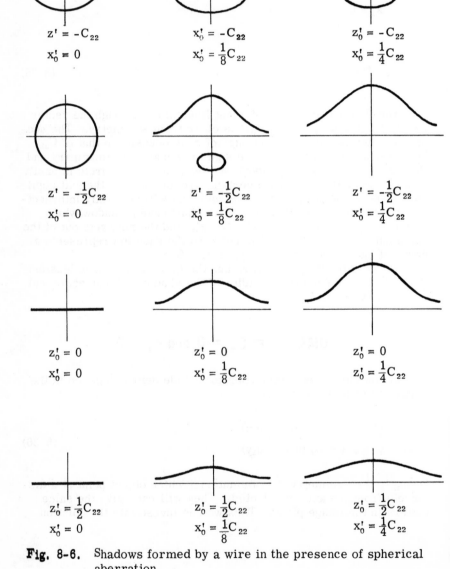

Fig. 8-6. Shadows formed by a wire in the presence of spherical aberration.

the x axis without loss of generality and this will result in some
simplifications in the arithmetic involved.   Now we can write

$$x' - \beta'x = \Delta x' = C_{12}\{r_1^2\rho \sin^2 \phi + \tfrac{1}{2}r_1^2\rho\}$$

$$= \tfrac{1}{2}C_{12}r_1^2\rho\{2 \sin^2 \phi + 1\}$$

$$= -\tfrac{1}{2}C_{12}r_1^2\rho\{-1 - 2 \sin^2 \phi\}$$

$$= -\tfrac{1}{2}C_{12}r_1^2\rho\{-2 + 1 - 2 \sin^2 \phi\}$$

$$= -\tfrac{1}{2}C_{12}r_1^2\rho\{-2 + \cos 2\phi\}$$

or

$$\Delta x' - C_{12}r_1^2\rho = -\tfrac{1}{2}C_{12}r_1^2\rho \cos 2\phi \qquad (8\text{-}37)$$

and

$$y' - \beta'y = \Delta y' = C_{12}r_1^2\rho \sin \phi \cos \phi$$

$$= \tfrac{1}{2}C_{12}r_1^2\rho \sin 2\phi \qquad (8\text{-}38)$$

Now squaring and adding we find

$$\left(\Delta x' - C_{12}r_1^2\rho\right)^2 + \Delta y'^2 = \left(\tfrac{1}{2}C_{12}r_1^2\rho\right)^2 \qquad (8\text{-}39)$$

These represent circles and add up to the well-known coma pattern
(Fig. 8-7).
   For a point, at a distance ρ from the axis, and with all the
rays going through a circular annulus in the entrance pupil having a
radius r_1, the image will be a circle with radius $1/2C_{12}r_1^2\rho$ and
whose center is displaced by a distance $C_{12}r_1^2\rho$ along the x' axis.
   We see also that while the ray goes once around an annulus in
the entrance pupil (ϕ from 0 to 2π), the ray goes twice around the
circle in the image plane because of the angle 2ϕ in the equations
for x' and y' (Fig. 8-8).
   Let us now look at the aberrations of the wavefront

$$\Delta = c_4 u_1^1 u_3^1 = c_4 r_1^3\rho \sin \phi$$

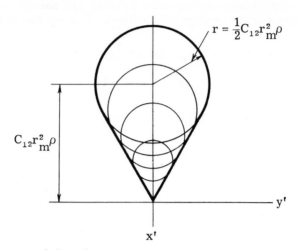

Fig. 8-7.   Coma in the paraxial image plane.

Here the situation is that for $0 < \phi < \pi$, Δ is positive and for $\pi < \phi < 2\pi$ the value of Δ is negative. It is clearly seen that the wavefront aberration Δ has the form shown in Fig. 8-9.

If we put a wire in this bundle and use the same symbols as before, defining x_0' as the distance from the paraxial image point, we find $x' - \beta'x = x_0'$

$$x_0' = z_0'x_1 + C_{12}\{xx_1^2 + \tfrac{1}{2}xx_1^2 + \tfrac{1}{2}xy_1^2\}$$

$$= z_0'x_1 + \underline{C}_{12}\{3x_1^2 + y_1^2\}$$

where

$$\underline{C}_{12} = \frac{C_{12}x}{2} \tag{8-40}$$

This is an ellipse with its axis parallel to the x_1 and y_1 axes and its center on the x axis (Fig. 8-10).

It is interesting to see what happens when the wire is parallel to the meridional plane (the plane going through the object point and the optical axis, in our case the x-z plane). If we call the distance from the wire to the paraxial image plane y_0' we find

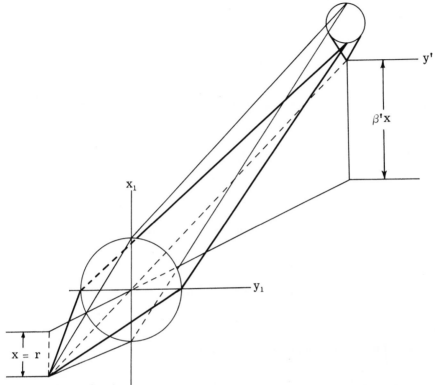

Fig. 8-8. Paths of rays through an optical system having coma.

$$y_0 = z_0' y_1 + C_{12} x x_1 y_1$$
$$= z_0' y_1 + 2\underline{C}_{12} x_1 y_1$$
$$= y_1 \{ z_0' + 2\underline{C}_{12} x_1 \} \qquad\qquad (8\text{-}41)$$

This is an equilateral hyperbola with its asymptotes parallel to the x_1 and y_1 axes. The center of the hyperbola is located on the x_1 axis and at a distance $-z_0/2C_{12}$ from the origin (Fig. 8-11).

ASTIGMATISM AND FIELD CURVATURE $C_{20} \neq 0; C_{11} \neq 0$
$$c_2 \neq 0; c_3 \neq 0$$

For reasons which will become clear we shall take these coefficients together.

We have, again taking our point on the x axis

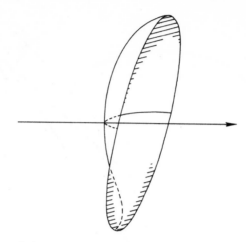

Fig. 8-9. Shape of wavefront in presence of coma.

$$x' - \beta'x = \beta_1'\frac{x_1}{r}z' + C_{20}u_1x_1 + C_{11}u_2x$$

$$y' - \beta'y = \beta_1'\frac{y_1}{r}z' + C_{20}u_1y_1 \tag{8-42}$$

Introducing polar coordinates we find

$$\Delta x' = \beta_1'\frac{z'}{r}r_1 \sin \phi + \frac{1}{2}C_{20}r\rho^2 \sin \phi + C_{11}r\rho^2 \sin \phi$$

$$\Delta y' = \beta_1'\frac{z'}{r}r_1 \cos \phi + \frac{1}{2}C_{20}r_1\rho^2 \cos \phi \tag{8-43}$$

$$\Delta x' = r_1\left\{\beta_1'\frac{z'}{r} + \rho^2(\frac{1}{2}C_{20} + C_{11})\right\} \sin \phi$$

$$\Delta y' = r_1\{\beta_1'\frac{z'}{r} + \frac{1}{2}\rho^2C_{20}\} \cos \phi \tag{8-44}$$

By squaring and adding we find

$$\frac{\Delta x'^2}{r_1^2\{\beta_1'\frac{z'}{r} + \rho^2(\frac{1}{2}C_{20} + C_{11})\}^2} + \frac{\Delta y'^2}{r_1^2\{\beta_1'\frac{z'}{r} + \frac{1}{2}\rho^2C_{20}\}^2} = 1 \tag{8-45}$$

This is an ellipse with its major axes given by

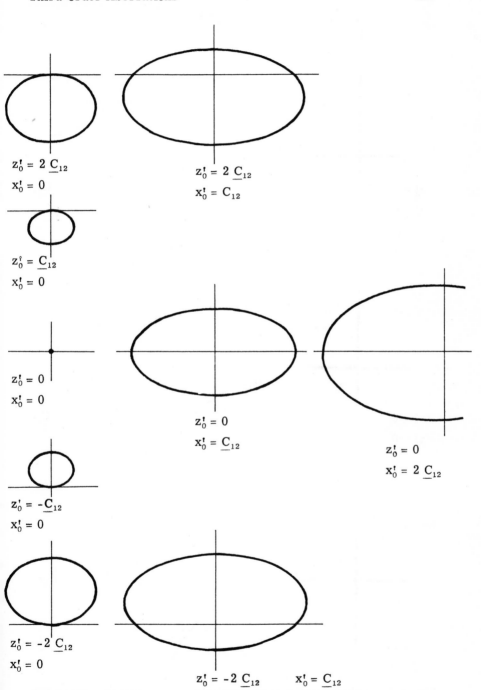

Fig. 8-10. Shadows of a wire perpendicular to a meridional plane in the presence of coma.

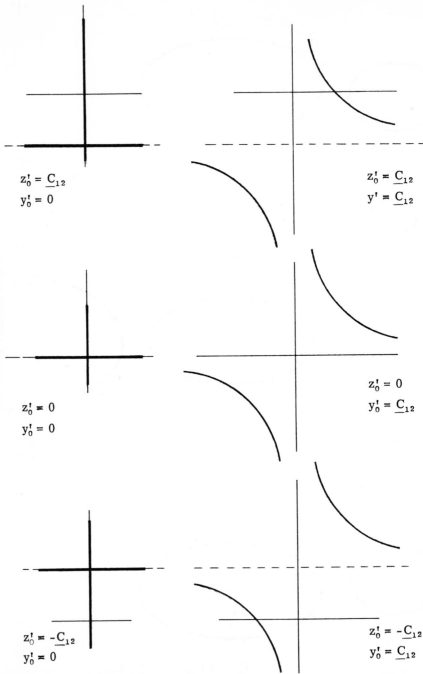

Fig. 8-11. Shadows of a wire parallel to a meridional plane in the presence of coma.

$$A = r_1 \left\{ \beta_1' \frac{z'}{r} + \rho^2 (\frac{1}{2} C_{20} + C_{11}) \right\}$$
$$B = r_1 \{ \beta_1' \frac{z'}{r} + \frac{1}{2} \rho^2 C_{20} \}$$

(8-46)

In the paraxial image plane we have the ellipse given by z = 0. If we defocus there are three cases of interest:
1. The position where A = 0. This is the tangential focal line.

$$z_T' = -\frac{1}{2} \frac{r}{\beta_1'} \rho^2 (C_{20} + 2C_{11})$$

(8-47)

2. The position where B = 0. This is the meridional focal line.

$$z_M' = -\frac{1}{2} \frac{r}{\beta_1'} \rho^2 C_{20}$$

(8-48)

3. The position where the ellipse reduces to a circle or A = B.
The only time we get an answer is when we take opposite signs for the two square roots.

$$\beta_1' \frac{z'}{r} + \rho^2 (\frac{1}{2} C_{20} + C_{11}) = -\beta_1' \frac{z'}{r} - \frac{1}{2} \rho^2 C_{20}$$
$$z_C' = -\frac{r\rho^2}{2\beta_1'} (C_{20} + C_{11})$$

(8-49)

This is halfway between the two focal lines, which is easily seen:

$$\frac{z_T' + z_M'}{2} = \frac{r\rho^2}{2\beta_1'} (C_{20} + C_{11})$$

(8-50)

(See Fig. 8-12.)
To see that the above coefficients also represent field curvature, we look into the equation for z' for the circle shown in Fig. 8-13.

$$h^2 + (z' - r)^2 = r^2$$
$$z' = \frac{h^2}{2r} + \dots$$

Comparing this with the formula for z_T' and z_M', remembering

Fig. 8-12. Astigmatic bundle.

that in this case the coordinate h is given by $\beta'\rho$ we find

$$R'_M = \frac{1}{r'_M} = -\frac{r}{\beta'^2\beta'_1}C_{20}$$

$$R'_T = \frac{1}{r'_T} = -\frac{r}{\beta'^2\beta'_1}(C_{20} + 2C_{11}) \qquad (8-51)$$

$$R'_C = \frac{1}{r'_C} = -\frac{r}{\beta'^2\beta'_1}(C_{20} + C_{11})$$

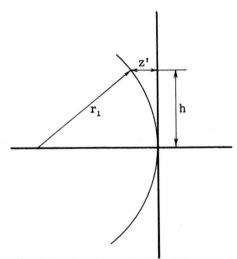

Fig. 8-13. Image curvature.

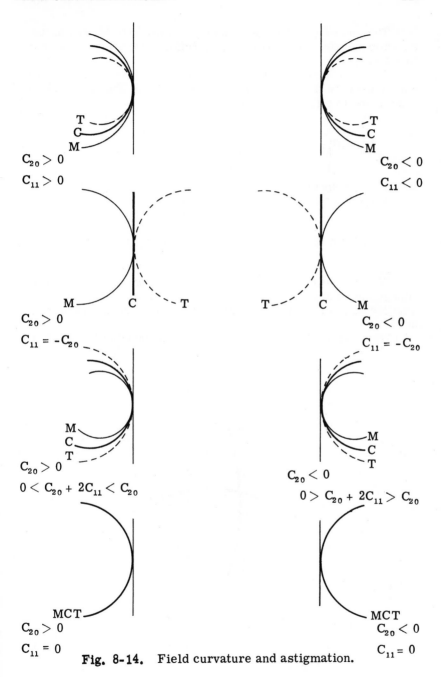

$$C_{20} > 0$$
$$C_{11} > 0$$

$$C_{20} < 0$$
$$C_{11} < 0$$

$$C_{20} > 0$$
$$C_{11} = -C_{20}$$

$$C_{20} < 0$$
$$C_{11} = -C_{20}$$

$$C_{20} > 0$$
$$0 < C_{20} + 2C_{11} < C_{20}$$

$$C_{20} < 0$$
$$0 > C_{20} + 2C_{11} > C_{20}$$

$$C_{20} > 0$$
$$C_{11} = 0$$

$$C_{20} < 0$$
$$C_{11} = 0$$

Fig. 8-14. Field curvature and astigmation.

This shows that the coefficient C_{20} is directly related to the curvature of the plane where the meridional astigmatic lines come to a focus.

The coefficient C_{11} is directly related to the difference in curvature between the planes where the meridional and sagittal focal lines come to a focus because

$$R'_T - R'_M = -\frac{2r}{\beta'^2\beta'_1}C_{11} \tag{8-52}$$

In Fig. 8-14 special cases are shown.

The form of the wavefront is given by

$$\Delta = c_2 u'_1 u'_3 + \frac{1}{2}c_3 u'^2_2 = \frac{1}{4}c_2 \rho'^2 r'^2_1 + \frac{1}{2}c_3 \rho'^2 r'^2_1 \sin^2 \phi \tag{8-53}$$

We see that there is, for every off-axis point, a deviation except in the center of the wavefront. The deviation for $\phi = 0°$ is smaller than for $\phi = 90°$ for a given r'_1. The form is shown in Fig. 8-15.

What happens when we put a wire in the bundle? Again defin-

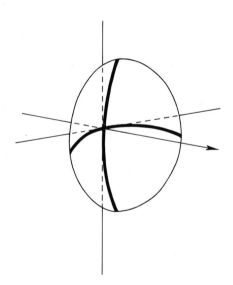

Fig. 8-15. Astigmatic wavefront.

ing x_0' and z_0' as we did above we have

$$x_0' = \frac{z_0'}{r}x_1' + \frac{1}{2}C_{20}(x^2 + y^2)x_1' + C_{11}(xx_1' + yy_1')x$$

or   (8-54)

$$y_1' = -\frac{\left\{\frac{z_0'}{r} + \frac{1}{2}C_{20}(x^2 + y^2) + C_{11}x^2\right\}x_1'}{yx} + \frac{x_0'}{xy}$$

This is a straight shadow and changing z_0' will change only its direction. It will rotate completely around.

DISTORTION $C_{10} \neq 0$ or $c_1 \neq 0$

We have

$$x' - \beta'x = C_{10}u_1x = \frac{1}{2}C_{10}x^3$$
$$y' = 0$$ (8-55)

If we again take our object point on the x axis we see that all the rays focus in the same point but not in the paraxial image point. If $C_{10} > 0$ we have what is called pincushion-shaped distortion, and if $C_{10} < 0$ we have barrel-shaped distortion (Fig. 8-16).

It is clear that the equation for the wavefront

$$\Delta = c_1u_1'u_2'$$ (8-56)

represents a spherical wavefront, tipped with respect to the reference sphere.

Putting a wire in the bundle is also of no value because it cannot reveal a deviation from the wavefront unless we know exactly where the paraxial image point should be formed, and, knowing this, all there is to know is known.

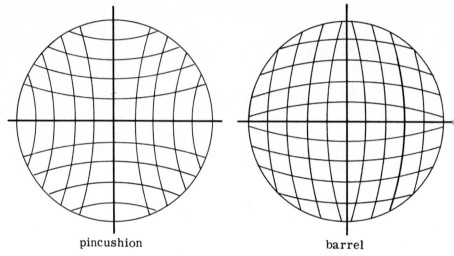

pincushion   barrel

Fig. 8-16. Distortion.

Chapter 9

THE NUMERICAL CALCULATION OF THE THIRD-ORDER ABBERATION COEFFICIENTS

The next problem is how to find the coefficients $C_{i,j}$ for a given optical system.

We have already found the first paraxial terms in the power series. We now want to find the next coefficients in this series. Paraxially we found

$$\begin{bmatrix} \underline{\alpha}' \\ h' \end{bmatrix} = \begin{bmatrix} \dfrac{1}{\beta'} & -a \\ 0 & \beta' \end{bmatrix} \begin{bmatrix} \underline{\alpha} \\ h \end{bmatrix}$$

The power series in general will again look like

$$\underline{\alpha}' = \frac{1}{\beta'}\underline{\alpha} - ah + d_1\underline{\alpha}^3 + d_2\underline{\alpha}^2h + d_3\underline{\alpha}h^2 + d_4h^3$$

$$h' = \beta'h + e_1\underline{\alpha}^3 + e_2\underline{\alpha}^2h + e_3\underline{\alpha}h^2 + e_4h^3$$

(9-1)

This we can write in matrix form as

$$\begin{bmatrix} \underline{\alpha}' \\ h' \\ \underline{\alpha}'^3 \\ \underline{\alpha}'^2h' \\ \underline{\alpha}'h'^2 \\ h'^3 \end{bmatrix} = \begin{bmatrix} \dfrac{1}{\beta'} & -a & d_1 & d_2 & d_3 & d_4 \\ 0 & \beta' & e_1 & e_2 & e_3 & e_4 \\ 0 & 0 & \dfrac{1}{\beta'^3} & -3\dfrac{a}{\beta'^2} & 3\dfrac{a^2}{\beta'} & -a^3 \\ 0 & 0 & 0 & \dfrac{1}{\beta'} & 2a & a^2\beta' \\ 0 & 0 & 0 & 0 & \beta' & -a\beta'^2 \\ 0 & 0 & 0 & 0 & 0 & \beta'^3 \end{bmatrix} \begin{bmatrix} \underline{\alpha} \\ h \\ \underline{\alpha}^3 \\ \underline{\alpha}^2h \\ \underline{\alpha}h^2 \\ h^3 \end{bmatrix}$$

(9-2)

The coefficients in the matrix are easily found by taking the first two equations and bringing them to the proper power. For instance

$$\underline{\alpha}'^3 = (\frac{1}{\beta'}\underline{\alpha} - ah + d_1\underline{\alpha}^3 + d_2\underline{\alpha}^2h + d_3\underline{\alpha}h^2 + d_4h^3)^3 \tag{9-3}$$

In doing this all the terms with coefficients d_i in Eq. (9-3) will produce terms of a power greater than 3 and can be neglected in our approximation. Thus the above equation becomes

$$\underline{\alpha}'^3 = (\frac{1}{\beta'}\underline{\alpha} - ah)^3$$
$$= \frac{1}{\beta'^3}\underline{\alpha}^3 - 3\frac{a}{\beta'^2}\underline{\alpha}^2h + 3\frac{a^2}{\beta'}\underline{\alpha}h^2 - a^3h^3 \tag{9-4}$$

which gives us the row for $\underline{\alpha}'^3$ in our matrix. The other rows are found in the same manner.

Now this matrix, if the coefficients d_i and e_i are known for one surface, should be multiplied with a matrix of the same form, representing the next surface. These multiplications will result in a matrix with elements composed of a multiplicity of sums of products. However, in doing so we find that the zeros in the matrix are helpful in simplifying these elements. We could simplify the problem even more if we could introduce more zeros. This is very easily done. As a matter of fact we have already done this when we discussed third-order aberrations. We did not use the variable α but the variable x_1 in a different reference plane. It is clear that we can again specify the ray completely by giving x_1, y_1, and x, y. With these new variables our matrix now reads

$$\begin{bmatrix} x' \\ x'_1 \\ u'_1x' \\ u'_1x'_1 \\ u'_2x' \\ u'_2x'_1 \\ u'_3x' \\ u'_3x'_1 \end{bmatrix} = \begin{bmatrix} \beta' & 0 & C_{10} & C_{20} & C_{11} & C_{21} & C_{12} & C_{22} \\ 0 & \beta'_1 & D_{10} & D_{20} & D_{11} & D_{21} & D_{12} & D_{22} \\ 0 & 0 & \beta'^3 & 0 & 0 & 0 & 0 & 0 \\ 0 & 0 & 0 & \beta'_1\beta'^2 & 0 & 0 & 0 & 0 \\ 0 & 0 & 0 & 0 & \beta'_1\beta'^2 & 0 & 0 & 0 \\ 0 & 0 & 0 & 0 & 0 & \beta'^2_1\beta' & 0 & 0 \\ 0 & 0 & 0 & 0 & 0 & 0 & \beta'^2_1\beta' & 0 \\ 0 & 0 & 0 & 0 & 0 & 0 & 0 & \beta'^3_1 \end{bmatrix} \begin{bmatrix} x \\ x_1 \\ u_1x \\ u_1x_1 \\ u_2x \\ u_2x_1 \\ u_3x \\ u_3x_1 \end{bmatrix} \tag{9-5}$$

and

$$
\begin{bmatrix} y' \\ y'_1 \\ u'_1 y' \\ u'_1 y'_1 \\ u'_2 y' \\ u'_2 y'_1 \\ u'_3 y' \\ u'_3 y'_1 \end{bmatrix}
=
\begin{bmatrix}
\beta' & 0 & C_{10} & C_{20} & C_{11} & C_{21} & C_{12} & C_{22} \\
0 & \beta'_1 & D_{10} & D_{20} & D_{11} & D_{21} & D_{12} & D_{22} \\
0 & 0 & \beta'^3 & 0 & 0 & 0 & 0 & 0 \\
0 & 0 & 0 & \beta'_1\beta'^2 & 0 & 0 & 0 & 0 \\
0 & 0 & 0 & 0 & \beta'_1\beta'^2 & 0 & 0 & 0 \\
0 & 0 & 0 & 0 & 0 & \beta'^2_1\beta' & 0 & 0 \\
0 & 0 & 0 & 0 & 0 & 0 & \beta'^2_1\beta' & 0 \\
0 & 0 & 0 & 0 & 0 & 0 & 0 & \beta'^3_1
\end{bmatrix}
\begin{bmatrix} y \\ y_1 \\ u_1 y \\ u_1 y_1 \\ u_2 y \\ u_2 y_1 \\ u_3 y \\ u_3 y_1 \end{bmatrix}
\qquad (9\text{-}6)
$$

We can go even further and introduce new variables in such a way that elements of the principal diagonal in this matrix become ones. This procedure will not be demonstrated. It amounts to using the right length units with which to measure x and x_1, and y and y_1.

We now have to find the values for the coefficients $C_{i,j}$. If we know the configuration of the system this reduces to the problem of finding the coefficients for a single surface, as shown above, and using the right variables in the power series expansion. This is in principle a simple, although lengthy, calculation. We shall not attempt to give it in all details at this time. Before we give the results, however, it is worthwhile to investigate the mathematical form in which we should arrange the coefficients to make the calculations as easy as possible.

Probably one of the easiest forms is one in which the coefficients are reduced into their factors. A clue to the factors lies in the aplanatic points. Here we have a situation where nearly all aberrations are equal to zero. If we can find factors which are equal to zero ($C_{i,j} = 0$) in the aplanatic points, we should be able to reduce the coefficients in these factors. There are possible difficulties with the coefficients for distortion and field curvature because these aberrations still exist in the aplanatic points.

Referring to Fig. 6-2, let us see what factors we can find which fulfill the above requirements.

We see that the three aplanatic points are:

a. The vertex of the surface (Fig. 9-1): Here we have the situation where

$$h = 0 \qquad \text{by definition} \qquad (9\text{-}7)$$

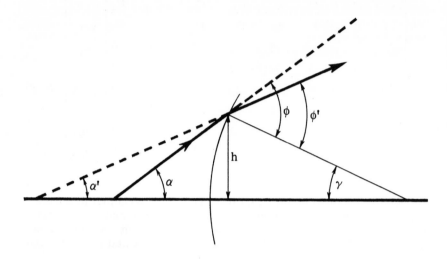

Fig. 9-1.   Refraction of a paraxial ray.

   b.   The center of curvature of the surface (Fig. 9-1): Here
we shall define

$$d = \alpha - \alpha' \qquad\qquad (9\text{-}8)$$

For the purpose of ease in calculation we shall use this in the form

$$d = \phi - \phi' \qquad\qquad (9\text{-}9)$$

These two are equal because (Fig. 9-1)

$$\alpha + \gamma = \phi$$
$$\alpha' + \gamma = \phi'$$

By subtraction we get

$$\phi - \phi' = \alpha - \alpha' \qquad\qquad (9\text{-}10)$$

c. The third set of points are at distances $\mu' r/\mu$ and $\mu r/\mu'$ from the center of curvature (Fig. 6-2). We are investigating an object point on axis so in this case the line CB in our figure represents the optical axis.

We have already proved that

$$\alpha = CBP = \phi'$$

and

$$\alpha' = CAP = \phi$$

Then

$$\frac{CA}{\phi'} = \frac{PC}{\alpha'}$$

$$\frac{CA}{\alpha} = \frac{PC}{\alpha'}$$

$$\frac{\frac{\mu}{\mu'} r}{\alpha} = \frac{r}{\alpha'}$$

$$\frac{\alpha'}{\mu'} = \frac{\alpha}{\mu}$$

We now have

$$\frac{\alpha}{\mu} - \frac{\alpha'}{\mu'} = 0$$

which gives us a third factor which we shall call

$$e = \left(\frac{\alpha}{\mu} - \frac{\alpha'}{\mu'} \right) \left(\frac{\mu\mu'}{\mu' - \mu} \right) \tag{9-11}$$

We can define the same quantities with respect to a ray going through the other reference plane, and we shall denote these quantities by

h', d', and e'

With the above-introduced quantities any ray defined by its intersection with the reference planes can now be described. (The primes in this case are not used in the conventional way and this fact should be carefully noted.)

The introduction of the above factors in this particular form was done because they are easily calculated with a paraxial ray tracing scheme introduced by Thomas Smith.

If we have a ray making an angle α_i with the axis (Fig. 9-2) and an entrance height h_i on the ith surface which has a radius r_i, we see that the angle ϕ_i is found paraxially by the relationship

$$\phi_i = \alpha_i + R_i h_i \tag{9-12}$$

With Snell's law we can calculate ϕ_i'

$$\phi_i' = \frac{\mu_i}{\mu_i'}\phi_i \tag{9-13}$$

Now d and e are given by

$$d_i = \phi_i - \phi_i'$$
$$e_i = \alpha_i + \phi_i' \tag{9-14}$$

The angle α_i' is given by the relationship

$$\alpha_i' = \alpha_i - d_i \tag{9-15}$$

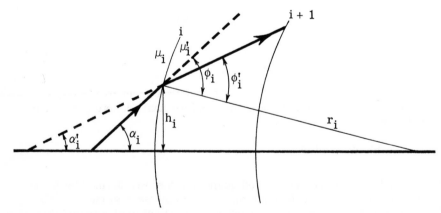

Fig. 9-2. Paraxial ray refracted by two surfaces.

For the translation to the i + 1th surface we find from the paraxial translation matrix

$$\alpha_i' = \alpha_{i+1}$$

$$h_{i+1} = h_i + t_i'\alpha_{i+1} \tag{9-16}$$

This procedure is easily handled in an arrangement shown in Table 9-1.

We shall now give the procedure (without proof) for calculating the $C_{i,j}$. (Quantities without subscripts refer to the system as a whole. Quantities with a subscript refer to the surface denoted by the subscript.)

Trace one ray paraxially through the axial point of the object making an angle $\alpha = G$ with the axis, where

$$G = \frac{\mu'}{\mu}\beta' \tag{9-17}$$

Trace one ray through the axial point of the second reference plane making an angle $\chi = S$ with the axis, where

$$S = \frac{\mu'}{\mu}\beta_1' \tag{9-18}$$

A check on the calculation is furnished by the fact that α' and χ' are then both equal to +1.

Also define the quantities

$$P_i = \frac{\mu_i \mu_i'}{\mu_i' - \mu_i} \qquad J_i = \frac{a_i}{\mu_i \mu_i'} \tag{9-19}$$

We now define the aberration coefficients by [notice that these are slightly different from those in Eqs. (8-22) and (8-23)]

$$\mu'x' = G\mu x + \frac{c_{10}}{2}(x^2 + y^2)x + \frac{c_{20}}{2}(x^2 + y^2)x_1$$

$$+ c_{11}(xx_1 + yy_1)x + c_{21}(xx_1 + yy_1)x_1$$

$$+ \frac{c_{12}}{2}(x_1^2 + y_1^2)x + \frac{c_{22}}{2}(x_1^2 + y_1^2)x_1 \tag{9-20}$$

$$\mu'y' = G\mu y + \frac{c_{10}}{2}(x^2 + y^2)y + \frac{c_{20}}{2}(x^2 + y^2)y_1$$

$$+ c_{11}(xx_1 + yy_1)y + c_{21}(xx_1 + yy_1)y_1$$

$$+ \frac{c_{12}}{2}(x_1^2 + y_1^2)y + \frac{c_{22}}{2}(x_1^2 + y_1^2)y_1 \qquad (9\text{-}21)$$

Instead of $C_{i,j}$ we use $c_{i,j}$ to indicate the difference in variables in the power series. They are now measured in different length units.

The other terms in these equations are defined in the following way:

$$x = \frac{(GJ\mu x)}{S - G} \qquad (9\text{-}22)$$

$$x_1 = \frac{(SJ\mu x_1)}{S - G} \qquad (9\text{-}23)$$

$$y = \frac{(GJ\mu y)}{S - G} \qquad (9\text{-}24)$$

$$y_1 = \frac{(GJ\mu y_1)}{S - G} \qquad (9\text{-}25)$$

The coefficients $c_{i,j}$ are calculated according to

$$c_{10} = \sum_1^n i \ h'_i d_i d'_i e'_i P_i + \frac{S - G}{J}(1 - S^2) \qquad (9\text{-}26)$$

$$c_{20} = \sum_1^n i - h_i d'^2_i e_i P_i - (\frac{S - G}{J})^2 \sum_1^n i \frac{R_i}{P_i} \qquad (9\text{-}27)$$

$$c_{11} = \sum_1^n i - h_i d'^2_i e_i P_i \qquad (9\text{-}28)$$

$$c_{21} = \sum_1^n i \ h_i d_i d'_i e_i P_i \qquad (9\text{-}29)$$

$$c_{12} = \sum_1^n i \ h_i d_i d'_i e_i P_i \qquad (9\text{-}30)$$

$$c_{22} = \sum_1^n i - h_i d^2_i e_i P_i \qquad (9\text{-}31)$$

The quantity $\sum_{i=1}^n \frac{R_i}{P_i}$ is called the Petzval sum.

As an example we shall take a lens given by

$$r_1 = +1 \qquad R_1 = +1$$
$$r_2 = \infty \qquad R_2 = 0$$
$$t' = 0.1000 \qquad \mu' = 1.5000$$

From this we calculate

$$a_1 = (1.5 - 1)(+1) = 0.5$$
$$a_2 = (1 - 1.5)0 = 0$$
$$\underline{t'} = 0.06667$$

and thus

$$\begin{bmatrix} 1 & 0 \\ 0 & 1 \end{bmatrix} \begin{bmatrix} 1 & 0 \\ 0.06667 & 1 \end{bmatrix} \begin{bmatrix} 1 & -0.5 \\ 0 & 1 \end{bmatrix}$$

$$= \begin{bmatrix} 1 & 0 \\ 0 & 1 \end{bmatrix} \begin{bmatrix} 1 & -0.5 \\ 0.06667 & 0.96666 \end{bmatrix}$$

$$= \begin{bmatrix} 1 & -0.5 \\ 0.06667 & 0.96666 \end{bmatrix}$$

$$f' = \frac{1}{a} = 2.0000$$

$$\ell'_F = \frac{c}{a} = \frac{0.96666}{0.5} = 1.93332$$

$$\ell'_H = \frac{c - 1}{a} = -0.06668$$

$$\ell'_F = -\frac{b}{a} = -2.000$$

$$\ell_H = \frac{1 - b}{a} = 0$$

Let us take an object with

$$\beta' = -0.5 \qquad G = -0.5$$
$$\beta'_1 = +1 \qquad S = +1$$

Table 9-1

		Object Ray		Reference Plane Ray	
System Data	r	1	∞	1	∞
	u	1.0000	1.5000	1.0000	1.5000
	u'	1.5000	1.0000	1.5000	1.0000
	$R = \dfrac{1}{r}$	1	0	1	0
	$\dfrac{u}{u'}$	0.66667	1.5	0.66667	1.5
	t'	0.1		0.1	
Ray Data	h	-3.0000	-2.93333	0	0.06667
	$\dfrac{t'\alpha'}{h_{i+1}}$ +	0.06667		0.06667	
		-2.93333		0.06667	
	α	-0.50000	0.66665	1.0000	0.66667
	$\dfrac{Rh}{\phi}$ +	-3.0000		0	
		-3.5	0.66665	1.0000	0.66667
	$\dfrac{u}{u'}\phi = \phi'$	-2.33335	0.99998	0.66667	1.00001
	d −	-1.16665	-0.33333	0.33333	-0.33334
	α	-0.5	0.66665	1.00000	0.66667
	$\dfrac{-d}{\alpha' = \alpha_{i-1}}$ +	+1.16665	0.33333	-0.3333	0.33334
		0.66665	0.99998	0.66667	1.00001
	α	-0.5000	0.66665	1.00000	0.66667
	$\dfrac{\phi'}{e}$ +	-2.33335	0.99998	0.66667	1.00000
		-2.83335	1.66663	1.66667	1.66667
	$P = \dfrac{uu'}{u'-u}$	3	-3	3	-3

Now we have

$$\frac{1}{\underline{s}'} = \frac{1}{\underline{s}} + a$$

or

$$1 = \frac{\underline{s}'}{\underline{s}} + \underline{s}'a$$

or

$$\underline{s}' = \frac{1 - \beta'}{a}$$

$$= \frac{1 + 0.5}{0.5} = 3.000$$

$$\frac{\underline{s}'}{\underline{s}} = \beta' \quad \text{or} \quad \underline{s} = \frac{\underline{s}'}{\beta'}$$

or

$$\underline{s} = \frac{3}{-0.5} = -6$$

We now trace the two rays. This is shown in Tables 9-1 and 9-2.

Table 9-2

hP	-9	8.800
heP	25.500	14.666
hdeP	-29.759	4.884
hd²eP	34.729	1.626
hdd'eP	-9.910	-1.626
hd'²eP	2.831	1.628
h'e'P	0	-0.33336
h'dd'e'P	0	-0.03704
$\dfrac{R_i}{P_i}$	0.333	0

$$\frac{S - G}{J} = 3$$

$$1 - S^2 = 0$$

$$\sum_{i=1}^{n} \frac{R_i}{P_i} = 0.333$$

$$\frac{S - G^2}{J} \sum_{i=1}^{n} \frac{R_i}{P_i} = 2.331$$

$$c_{10} = -0.03704$$
$$c_{20} = -2.831 - 1.628 - 2.331 = -6.790$$
$$c_{11} = -4.459$$
$$c_{21} = -9.910 - 1.626 = -11.536$$
$$c_{12} = -11.536$$
$$c_{22} = -34.729 - 1.626 = -36.355$$

The above rules are sufficient to calculate the third-order aberrations in most cases. There is, however, one case where the rules do not help and that is where G = 0, or, our object is at infinity. It is clear that in this case we have to take

$$\alpha_1 = 0$$

but h_1 is still undetermined. By taking the proper limits in this case we find (the angle α'_n has to equal +1)

$$h_1 = -\frac{1}{\mu_1 J_{1,n}} \tag{9-32}$$

Similarly we have in the case where S = 0

$$h'_1 = -\frac{1}{\mu_1 J_{1,n}} \tag{9-33}$$

Let us take as an example, a thin lens (t' = 0) of the following form:

$$r_1 = +0.3333 \quad \text{so} \quad R_1 = +3$$
$$r_2 = +1 \quad \text{so} \quad R_2 = +1$$
$$\mu = 1.5$$
$$G = 0$$
$$S = +1$$

Table 9-3

	Object ray		Reference ray	
R	3	1	3	1
$\frac{\mu}{\mu'}$	0.66667	1.5	0.66667	1.5
t'	0		0	
h	-1	-1	0	0
$\frac{t'\alpha'}{h_1}$ +	0 -1	0 0		
α	0	+1	+1	0.66667
$\frac{Rh}{\phi}$ +	-3 -3	-1 0	0 +1	0 0.66667
$\frac{\frac{\mu}{\mu'}\phi = \phi'}{d}$ -	-2 -1	0 0	+0.66667 0.33333	1 -0.33333
α	-0	+1	+1	0.66667
$\frac{-d}{\alpha'}$ +	+1 +1	0 +1	-0.33333 0.66667	0.33333 +1
α	0	+1	+1	0.66667
$\frac{\phi'}{e}$ +	-2 -2	0 +1	0.66667 1.66667	1 1.66667
P	+3	-3		

Then

$$a = 0.5(3 - 1) = +1$$

$$J = +1$$

$$c_{10} = \sum_{i=1}^{n} h_i' d_i d_i' e_i' P_i + \frac{S_{1,n} - G_{1,n}}{J_{1,n}}(1 - S_{1,n}^2)$$

$$= (0)(-1)(0.3333)(1.66667)(3) + (0)(0)(-0.33333)(1.66667)(-3)$$

$$= 0$$

$$c_{20} = \sum_{i=1}^{n} - h_i d_i'^2 e_i P_i - \left(\frac{S_{1,n} - G_{1,n}}{J_{1,n}}\right)^2 \sum_{i=1}^{n} \frac{R_i}{P_i}$$

$$= -(-1)(0.33333)^2(-2)3 - (-1)(-0.33333)^2(+1)(-3)$$
$$- (1 - 0.33333)$$

$$= -1.66667$$

$$c_{11} = \sum_{i=1}^{n} - h_i d_i'^2 e_i P_i$$

$$= -1$$

$$c_{21} = \sum_{i=1}^{n} h_i d_i d_i' e_i P_i = c_{12}$$

$$= (-1)(-1)(0.33333)(-2)(3) + (-1)(0)$$

$$= -2$$

$$c_{22} = \sum_{i=1}^{n} - h_i d_i^2 e_i P_i$$

$$= -(-1)(-1)^2(-2)(3) - (-1)(0)$$

$$= -6$$

Because of the fact that $c_{21} = c_{12}$ and

$$c_{20} = c_{11} - \left\{\frac{S_{1,n} - G_{1,n}}{J_{1,n}}\right\}\sum_{i=1}^{n} \frac{R_i}{P_i}$$

in all cases, it is much easier to investigate the meridional aberration coefficients only. In order to arrive at the relationships between the meridional coefficients and the coefficients $c_{i,j}$ we set in Eq. (9-20),

$$y = 0 \quad \text{and} \quad y_1 = 0$$

Then

$$\mu'x' = G\mu x - \frac{c_{10}}{2}x^3 + \frac{c_{20}}{2}x^2x_1 + c_{11}x^2x_1 + c_{21}xx_1^2$$

$$+ \frac{c_{12}}{2}x_1^2x + \frac{c_{22}}{2}x_1^3$$

$$= G\mu x + \frac{c_{10}}{2}x^3 + \frac{1}{2}(c_{20} + 2c_{11})x^2x_1$$

$$+ \frac{1}{2}(2c_{21} + c_{12})xx_1^2 + \frac{c_{22}}{2}x_1^3 \tag{9-34}$$

If we now define the meridional coefficients in the following way:

$$\mu'x' = G\mu x + \frac{1}{2}m_1x^3 + \frac{1}{2}m_2x^2x_1 + \frac{1}{2}m_3xx_1^2 + \frac{1}{2}m_4x_1^3 \tag{9-35}$$

then compare Eq. (9-34) with Eqs. (9-35) and (9-26) through (9-31) and we find

$$m_1 = c_{10} = \sum_{i=1}^{n} h_i'd_id_i'e_i'P_i + \frac{S_{1,n} - G_{1,n}}{J_{1,n}}(1 - S_{1,n}^2) \tag{9-36}$$

$$m_2 = c_{20} + 2c_{11} = -3\sum_{i=1}^{n} h_id_i'^2e_iP_i - \frac{S_{1,n} - G_{1,n}}{J_{1,n}}$$

$$\cdot \sum_{i=1}^{n} \frac{R_i}{P_i} \tag{9-37}$$

$$m_3 = 2c_{21} + c_{12} = 3\sum_{i=1}^{n} h_id_id_i'e_iP_i \tag{9-38}$$

$$m_4 = c_{22} = -\sum_{i=1}^{n} h_id_i^2e_iP_i \tag{9-39}$$

The meridional or tangential field curvature R_m and the sagittal curvature R_s are found from the equations

$$R_m = \frac{\mu'J_{1,n}^2m_2}{(S_{1,n} - G_{1,n})} \tag{9-40}$$

$$R_s = \frac{R_m}{3} - \frac{2\mu'}{3}\sum_{i=1}^{n} \frac{R_i}{P_i} \tag{9-41}$$

For further study of this chapter see References 6, 12, 16, 17, 20, 21, 22, 23, 29, 35, 36, 42, 43, 47, 51, 56, 58, 60, 83, 90, 93, and 99.

Chapter 10

ABBERATIONS OF VARIOUS SYSTEMS

THIRD-ORDER ABERRATIONS OF A THIN LENS

In order to get some insight into the aberrations of lenses we shall investigate the easiest possible configuration, the thin lens.

We have already calculated the aberrations for one thin lens in the above example. If we would now change the form of the lens we would find a different set of values. Instead of calculating different cases (both different forms and different positions of the object plane) we could try to find a more general formula. We do this by using the above calculating method, but instead of using numerical values we substitute $G_{1,n}$ for α_1, etc., thus arriving at a general solution for this problem. This is a lengthy procedure and we will again omit all the details and give only the results.

Before doing this we shall introduce some new quantities.

$$M = \frac{1 + G}{1 - G} \tag{10-1}$$

$$\omega = \frac{1}{\mu} \tag{10-2}$$

$$\rho = R_1 + R_2 \tag{10-3}$$

The quantity ρ is called the shape factor of the lens. By giving the power, the shape factor, and the refractive index we completely describe the lens.

$$a = (\mu - 1)(R_1 - R_2) \quad \text{or} \quad a = (\mu - 1)R_1 - (\mu - 1)R_2$$

136

$$\rho = R_1 + R_2 \quad \text{or} \quad (\mu - 1)\rho = (\mu - 1)R_1 + (\mu - 1)R_2$$

By adding we find

$$a + (\mu - 1)\rho = 2(\mu - 1)R_1$$

or

$$R_1 = \frac{a + (\mu - 1)\rho}{2(\mu - 1)} \tag{10-4}$$

and

$$R_2 = \frac{a - (\mu - 1)\rho}{-2(\mu - 1)} \tag{10-5}$$

Changing ρ is sometimes called "bending" the lens.

In order to get a feeling for the magnitude of the aberrations it is customary to reduce the power of every lens to $+1$. In this way we can compare all lenses with each other easily. In our investigation of the thin lens we shall also restrict ourselves to the case where $\mu = 1.5$ and the entrance pupil is formed by the edge of the lens $(S = +1)$.

With the above restrictions the relations R_1 and R_2 [Eqs. (10-4) and (10-5)] become

$$R_1 = \frac{\rho}{2} + 1 \tag{10-6}$$

$$R_2 = \frac{\rho}{2} - 1 \tag{10-7}$$

Again with the same restrictions we find for

m_4 (spherical aberration)

$$m_4 = -\frac{1}{4}(G - 1)^4 \left\{ \frac{1}{(1 - \omega)^2} + (1 + 2\omega)\rho^2 - 4M(1 + \omega)\rho \right.$$

$$\left. + (3 + 2\omega)M^2 \right\} \tag{10-8}$$

If we plot m_4 as a function of ρ with M (or G) as a parameter we find a set of parabolas. A number of these are shown in Fig. 10-1.

We see that for $G = +1$ we have $m_4 = 0$ for all shape factors. We also see that for $G = +1/2$ and $G = +3/2$ the form of the lens still has very little influence on the value of m_4. This is important in the case of field lenses. Quite often we do not want the image directly in the field lens $(G = +1)$ because we shall then also see all

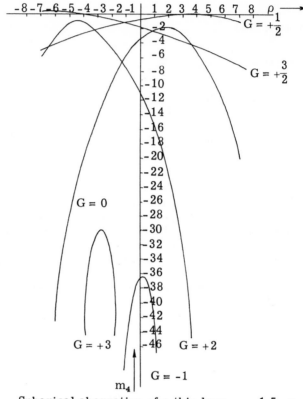

Fig. 10-1. Spherical aberration of a thin lens $\mu = 1.5$, $a = +1$.

the dust particles on the lens. Bringing the image just outside the lens (changing G slightly away from the value +1) does not influence the spherical aberration very much, regardless of the form of the lens.

m₃ (coma)

$$m_3 = \frac{3}{2}(G - 1)^3\left\{(1 + \omega)\rho + (2 + \omega)M\right\}$$

(10-9)

m_3 as a function of ρ, again using G as a parameter, gives a set of straight lines. A number of them are shown in Fig. 10-2. Again the ρ axis represents the case where $G = +1$.

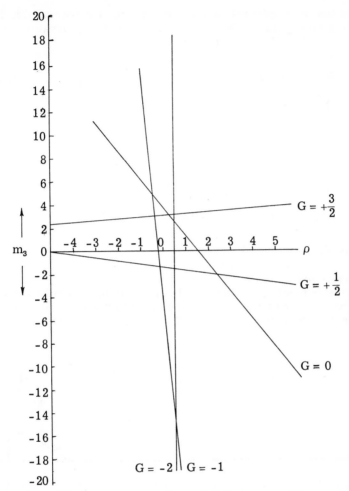

Fig. 10-2. m_3 coma for a thin lens $\mu = 1.5$, $a = +1$.

m_2 (astigmatism and field curvature)

$$m_2 = -(G - 1)^2(3 + \omega) \tag{10-10}$$

Here we see that the form of the lens is immaterial and that there is no way to remove astigmatism and field curvature. This holds also in the more general case where we combine several thin lenses into a thin system. Our formulas for the field curvature reduce in this case to

$$R_m = -(3 + \omega) \tag{10-11}$$

$$R_s = -(1 + \omega) \tag{10-12}$$

or for

$$n = 1.5$$

$$R_m = -3.667 \qquad r_m = -0.273$$

$$R_s = -1.667 \qquad r_s = -0.6$$

This is shown in Fig. 10-3.

m_1 (distortion) $m_1 = 0$

This is easily seen because in this case $h_i' = 0$ because $S = +1$. For the same reason it will also be equal to zero for all thin-lens systems if the pupil coincides with the system ($S = +1$).

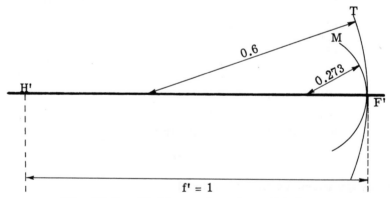

Fig. 10-3.   Field curvature for a thin lens.

THE SINGLE 'THICK' LENS

We shall now consider two important forms of "thick" lenses. The first one is shown in Fig. 10-4. In this lens the aplanatic points are used twice. If the first surface of the lens is flat and the object is placed at this surface, it is clear that the image formed by this first surface is aberration free. The second surface is again chosen in such a way that the object and image are aplanatic, as explained in Chap. 6. It can be shown that the thickness of the lens is then given by

$$t = -r(1 + \frac{1}{\mu})$$

(10-13)

and the over-all magnification of the total lens is

$$\beta' = \mu^2$$

(10-14)

The second type is shown in Fig. 10-5. Here the object is placed in the center of curvature of the first surface. The second surface acts in the same way as the second surface in the above lens. We see that

$$-r_1 + t = -r_2(1 + \frac{1}{\mu})$$

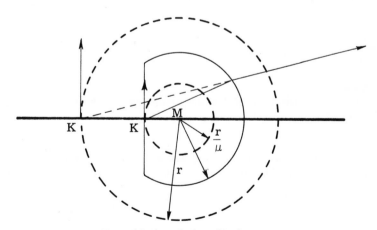

Fig. 10-4. Aplanatic lens.

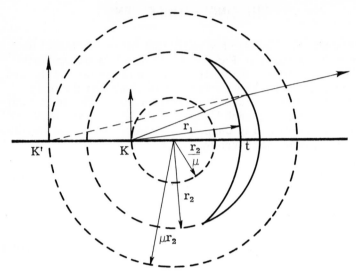

Fig. 10-5. Aplanatic lens.

or

$$t = (r_1 - r_2) - \frac{r_2}{\mu} \qquad\qquad (10\text{-}15)$$

In this case the total magnification is

$$\beta' = \mu \qquad\qquad (10\text{-}16)$$

Problem:
Prove that the magnifications given for the above two cases
are correct.

We see that the above lenses are aplanatic for only one given
value of μ and are therefore not corrected for color aberrations.

THE PLANE-PARALLEL PLATE

Although the plane-parallel plate is usually not referred to as
a lens, this seems to be the appropriate place to say a few words
about the aberrations introduced by it.

If we place a plane-parallel glass plate in a converging bundle
as shown in Fig. 10-6, we can consider K as an object which is
imaged by the plane-parallel plate in K'. Paraxially we then have

$$KK' = \frac{\mu - 1}{\mu}d \qquad\qquad (10\text{-}17)$$

where d is the thickness of the plate.

It is easily seen that each ray will enter and leave the plate
under the same angle, in other words the plate displaces the ray
but does not change its direction. However, it does introduce
spherical aberration. It is clear that color aberrations are also
introduced by the plate.

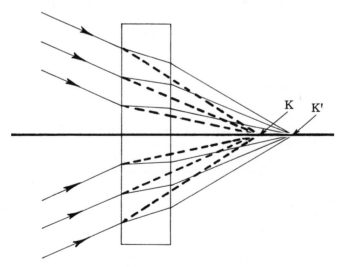

Fig. 10-6. Image formation through a plane-parallel plate.

ABBE'S SINE CONDITION

For the transformation of a real ray through an optical system we can write

$$\begin{bmatrix} L' \\ X' \end{bmatrix} = \begin{bmatrix} B & -A \\ -D & C \end{bmatrix} \begin{bmatrix} L \\ X \end{bmatrix} \tag{10-18}$$

By introducing two more translation matrices, just as we did in paraxial optics, we find

$$\begin{bmatrix} L' \\ x' \end{bmatrix} = \begin{bmatrix} \dfrac{1}{\beta'} & -A \\ 0 & \beta' \end{bmatrix} \begin{bmatrix} L \\ x \end{bmatrix} \tag{10-19}$$

where the ray coordinates refer to an object and image point on the ray. It is easily seen that for an optical system without aberrations the values of β' and A should be the same for each ray passing the system and they should be equal to the paraxial values β' and a for the system. Assuming an aberration-free system we can investigate the rays coming from the axial point of the object. In this case $x = 0$ and we have

$$L' = \frac{L}{\underline{\beta'}} = \frac{L}{\beta'}$$

Rays from an axial point are meridional rays by definition, and we can replace cos α by sin γ, where γ is the angle of the ray with the z axis when we select the x axis in such a way that the rays are in the x-z plane. The above relationship then reads

$$\frac{\mu' \sin \gamma}{\mu \sin \gamma} = \frac{1}{\beta'} \tag{10-20}$$

It can be shown that the image of a point around this axial point is also aberration free if the above condition is fulfilled. A deviation from this relation by actual rays is an indication of off-axis aberrations (coma). This relation is called the Abbe sine condition. It is customary to plot the deviations from the sine condition if one wants to show, graphically, the performance of a system. On pp.

147-150 we shall show the performance of various lens systems. There are three graphs for each system. The first one (a) will show (solid line) the relationship between the incidence height x_1 of the ray on the entrance pupil and the longitudinal spherical aberration for an object point on axis.

In the same figure the deviation from the sine condition is shown by a dashed line. In the next graph (b) we shall plot the position of the meridional (solid line) and tangential (dashed line) focal planes as a function of the field angle. In the third graph (c) we shall plot the distortion as a function of the field angle.

'THIN' DOUBLETS AND TRIPLETS

As was pointed out in the case of a single thin lens, the distortion is zero and we cannot correct for field curvature and astigmatism. The remaining aberrations are: (1) color aberration; (2) spherical aberration; (3) coma.

Let us first consider the case of a thin doublet. From the theory of color aberrations we know that we can correct these by the use of two thin lenses of different glass types. As was pointed out, it is only necessary to give the two components the appropriate powers for the given glasses. The form of both components is immaterial. We can make use of this fact to try to correct for spherical aberration and coma by "bending" each component. Usually both aberrations can be made zero simultaneously as far as the third-order approximation is concerned. A slight change in the actual form of the lenses will then usually give the desired balance between third- and higher-order aberrations.

It is clear, however, that in general the two components will then have a form such that $r_2 \neq r_3$, and it will be impossible to cement both components together in order to reduce reflection losses (Fig. 10-7a). However, different choices of glasses will give different solutions, and it is possible to start with a glass combination such that in the final solution $r_2 = r_3$ and both components can thus be cemented together (Fig. 10-7b).

Actually there are two solutions for each glass combination. The one usually chosen is the one with the crown (positive) component toward the object if the object is at infinity. It is also possible to have the flint (negative) component first. Most doublets are, however, of the first kind.

If we do not have the right combination of glasses available and we want to make a cemented system we can split the positive component into two components and place the negative one in between the positive ones. We again have enough degrees of freedom

(a)   (b)

Fig. 10-7. Doublets.

to demand from the solution that $r_2 = r_3$ and $r_4 = r_5$. In this way we have a cemented triplet.

Following are some examples. Starting with the glasses

$$\mu = 1.51678 \quad \nu = 60.7$$
$$\mu = 1.66755 \quad \nu = 41.9$$

we can design a thin uncemented doublet (Fig. 10-8) or a cemented triplet (Fig. 10-9). Note that the uncemented doublet has very steeply curved inner surfaces and changes in these curvatures change the aberrations very quickly. For this reason this is not a practical solution because the cost of fabrication would be excessive. Both cases are given for an F:4 lens.

In Figs. 10-10 and 10-11 solutions for a cemented doublet are shown. In order to design such a system we have to start with a proper combination of glasses. The combination we have chosen is

$$\mu = 1.51678 \quad \nu = 60.7$$
$$\mu = 1.70100 \quad \nu = 30.0$$

One is an F:4 and the other an F:2 system to show the difference in residual aberration with increasing aperture.

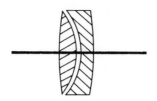

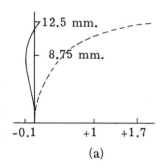

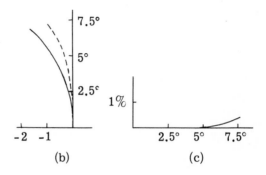

(a)   (b)   (c)

Surface	r	t'	μ_d	ν
1	62.088			
		5.728	1.51678	60.7
2	-23.566			
		0.019		
3	-24.156			
		2.864	1.66755	41.9
4	-89.449			

Fig. 10-8.   Uncemented doublet (designer: W. Brouwer, 1958).

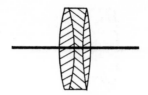

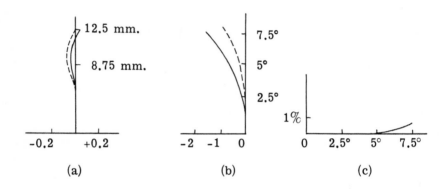

(a)   (b)   (c)

Surface	4	t'	μ_d	ν
1	55.830			
		4.436	1.51678	60.7
2	-39.070			
		2.465	1.66755	41.9
3	132.525			
		2.465	1.51678	60.7
4	-88.439			

Fig. 10-9. Cemented triplet (designer: W. Brouwer, 1958).

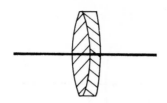

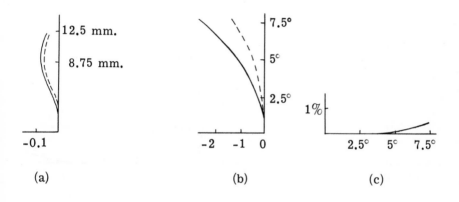

(a)   (b)   (c)

Surface	r	t'	μ_d	ν
1	61.070			
		4.044	1.51678	60.7
2	-47.107			
		2.022	1.70100	30.0
3	-127.098			

Fig. 10-10.   F:4 cemented doublet (designer: W. Brouwer, 1958).

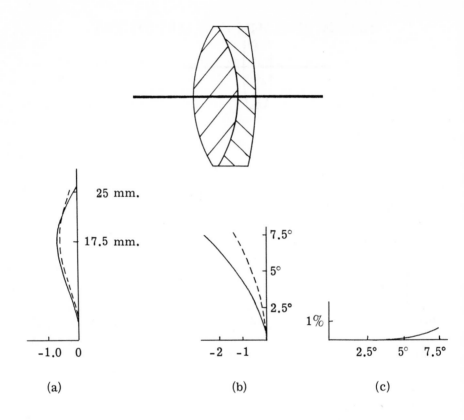

Surface	r	t'	μ_d	ν
1	62.278			
		12.391	1.51678	60.7
2	-49.654			
		6.195	1.70100	30.0
3	-124.237			

Fig. 10-11.   F:2 cemented doublet (designer: W. Brouwer, 1958).

FURTHER DEVELOPMENT OF LENS SYSTEMS

In order to correct for field curvature and astigmatism we have to depart from the thin lens. The first to realize this was J. Petzval in 1840. His solution, still called the Petzval lens, was two thin doublets (one cemented and one air-spaced) separated by an air space. For an example of this type of lens see Fig. 10-12.

It is also possible to design the second component as a cemented doublet. As an example see Fig. 10-13. This type of lens is still in use for portrait objectives and projectors. The field is relatively small but the lenses can be made with a large aperture.

The next improvement was introduced by H. Dennis Taylor in 1893. This is called the Cooke triplet. For an example of this lens see Fig. 10-14. We see that the field correction is now possible for much wider field angles; however, not with such high apertures as the Petzval lenses.

P. Rudolph introduced the Tessar around 1900. In this solution the last component in the Cooke triplet is a cemented doublet. Historically, Rudolph did not start from the Cooke triplet but from a different point of view. For an example of a Tessar see Fig. 10-15.

Now we can start to introduce more and more components and/or split single components into two or more cemented components. As an example of a very fast lens we show the R-Biotar (Fig. 10-16), designed by W. Merte in 1932.

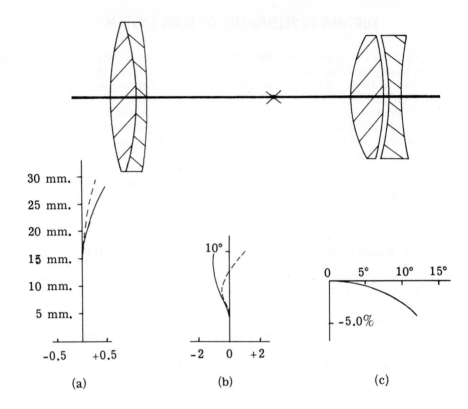

Surface	r	t'	μ_d	ν
1	78.4			
		11.9	1.5178	60.3
2	-70.1			
		2.4	1.6520	33.5
3	-403.7			
		89.5		
4	43.3			
		10.7	1.6135	59.4
5	-69.6			
		0.4		
6	-61.7			
		2.4	1.6520	33.5
7	152.0			

Fig. 10-12. Petzval (designer: A. Warmisham, English Patent No. 376025, 1932).

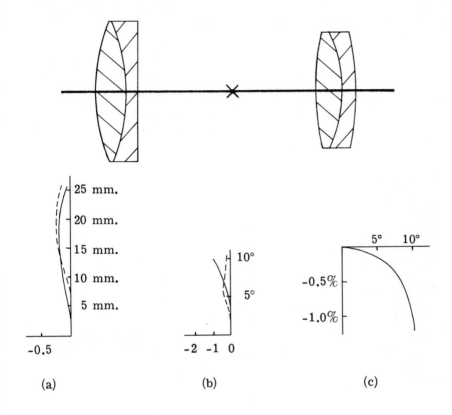

Surface	r	t'	μd	ν
1	73.7	12.0	1.5111	60.6
2	-73.7	3.5	1.6199	36.3
3	Plano	73.7		
4	67.4	11.0	1.5111	60.6
5	-38.0	2.5	1.6199	36.3
6	-155.0			

Fig. 10-13. Petzval (designer: R. Richter, German Patent No. 544429, 1930).

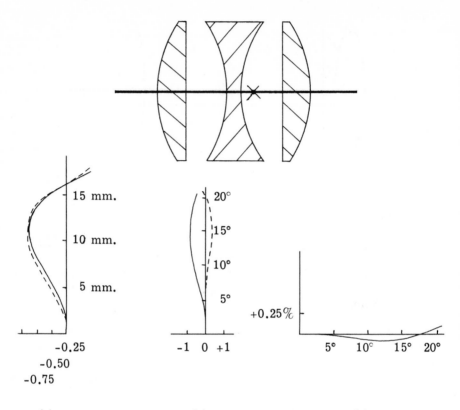

(a)   (b)   (c)

Surface	r	t'	μd	ν
1	40.1	6.0	1.613	58.5
2	-537.0	10.0		
3	-47.0	1.0	1.621	36.2
4	40.0	10.8		
5	234.5	6.0	1.613	58.5
6	-37.9			

Fig. 10-14.   Cooke triplet (designer: H. W. Lee, English Patent
No. 155640, 1919).

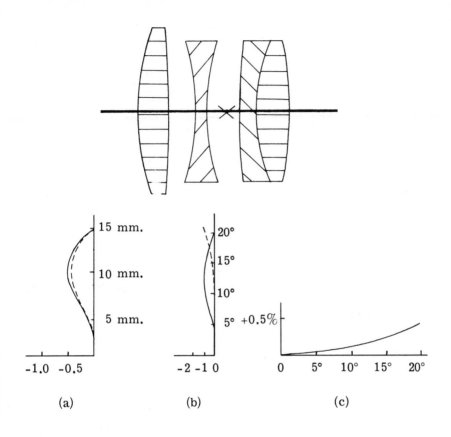

(a)   (b)   (c)

Surface	r	t'	μd	ν
1	32.4	6.0	1.6202	60.0
2	-579.8	6.6		
3	-58.5	2.9	1.5785	42.3
4	27.6	6.6		
5	579.8	2.2	1.5315	49.1
6	26.2	8.8	1.6202	60.0
7	-42.4			

Fig. 10-15. Tessar (designer: A. W. Tronnier, American Patent No. 2084714, 1937).

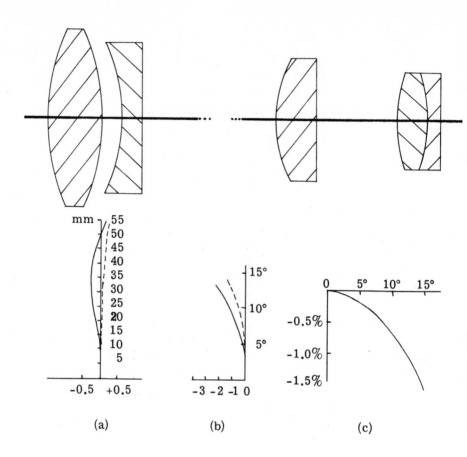

(a)   (b)   (c)

Surface	r	t'	μd	ν
1	135.1	30.0	1.6375	56.1
2	-183.0	0.2		
3	-129.0	11.7	1.7582	27.4
4	-1813.8	60.4		
5	97.7	23.8	1.4645	65.8
6	Plano	22.6		
7	60.2	15.1	1.6220	53.1
8	-59.8	3.4	1.7582	27.4
9	-369.2			

Fig. 10-16. R biotar (designer: W. Merte, German Patent No. 607631, 1932).

Chapter 11

SOME VISUAL INSTRUMENTS

THE EYE

We shall only describe those facts which have a bearing on the design factors of other instruments.

The resolving power of the eye is usually considered to be 1'. The eye is, however, much more sensitive to symmetry. The precision here is of the order of 5" (Fig. 11-1).

The point around which the eyeball rotates is located approximately 13 mm behind the cornea. The intereye distance is between 6 and 7 cm. The field of view of an eye at rest is considered to be 60°. The nearest point on which the eye can focus is considered to be 25 cm away.

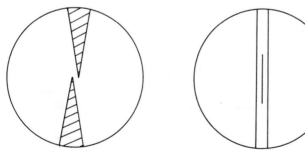

Fig. 11-1. Setting on symmetry.

THE LOUPE

The loupe is used to form enlarged visual images. If we use a loupe, we have to form an image of the object in such a way that the eye can look at it. This means that we have to form an image at infinity. In other words, we have to put the object in the object focal point of the loupe. For every instrument with a finite object distance having the image at infinity, we find that the linear magnification $\beta' = \infty$. What really counts here is not the linear magnification of the loupe alone, but how much bigger can we see the object with the aid of the loupe. This is called the loupe magnification. We will now derive a formula for the loupe magnification.

If we look at an object of height y (Fig. 11-2) with the naked eye, we can see this object under an angle α which can be at the most

$$\tan \alpha = \frac{y}{25}$$

With the aid of a loupe (Fig. 11-3) we have

$$\tan \gamma = \frac{y}{f}$$

The loupe magnification (V) is defined as

$$V = \frac{\tan \gamma}{\tan \alpha} = \frac{25}{f} \qquad (11\text{-}1)$$

if f is given in centimeters.

The actual field of view gets smaller as the magnification in-

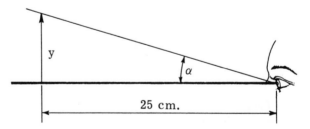

Fig. 11-2. The loupe magnification.

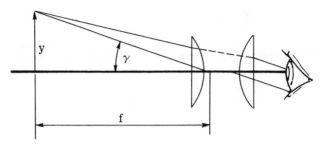

Fig. 11-3. The loupe magnification.

creases. The exit pupil of the loupe is formed by the pupil of the
eye. If we want a field bigger than 60° we have to move our eye.
For this reason the exit pupil is usually designed to be 25 mm behind the last surface to give the eye enough room to move.

Another important dimension is the distance between the object
and the front surface of the first lens of the loupe. The greater
this distance the more convenient it is to use the loupe. It is obvious that the field of view is dependent on the distance of the eye behind the loupe, i.e., the closer the eye, the bigger the field of view.
In this way we put the pupil of the eye in the position for which the
loupe was designed and corrected. Three of the better loupe designs are shown in Fig. 11-4.

THE TELESCOPE

The telescope is an instrument which presents to the eye an
enlarged image of distant objects. For all practical purposes the
object is at infinity. In order to present an image to the eye com-
fortably, it has to be formed again at infinity. In order to do this,
an optical system has to fulfill certain conditions. We will investigate these conditions first.

From the object-image relationship [Eq. (4-7)] we find

$$\frac{1}{\infty} = \frac{1}{\infty} + a \qquad\qquad (11\text{-}2)$$

or

$$a = 0$$

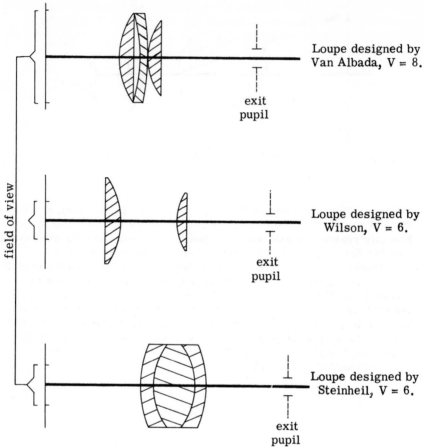

Fig. 11-4.   Various types of loupes.

Thus a telescopic system is a system with a power of 0.   The matrix of such a system is

$$\begin{bmatrix} b & 0 \\ -d & c \end{bmatrix}$$ (11-3)

and

$$bc = +1$$

If the object is at infinity all the rays from one single object point come into the system making the same angle with the axis. Suppose we take an object point such that the rays come in under an angle α with the optical axis. We find

$$\begin{bmatrix} \alpha' \\ x' \end{bmatrix} = \begin{bmatrix} b & 0 \\ -d & c \end{bmatrix} \begin{bmatrix} \alpha \\ x \end{bmatrix} \tag{11-5}$$

Thus all these rays come out of the system under an angle

$$\alpha' = b\alpha \tag{11-6}$$

and we see that all the rays emerge under the same angle, which they should, in order to put the image at infinity. The linear magnification is not important. It is clear, however, that the angular magnification γ is the important quantity, and from Eq. (11-6) it follows that

$$\gamma = b = \frac{1}{c} \tag{11-7}$$

Thus it turns out that the magnification γ equals the Gaussian constant b.

A telescopic system possesses another characteristic. If we put an object at a finite distance we have, according to Eqs. (3-13) and (3-16)

$$\beta' = c - \underline{\ell}'a = \frac{1}{b + \underline{\ell}a}$$

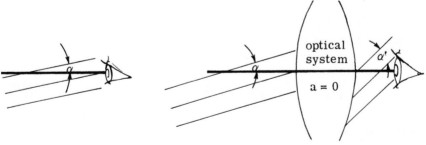

Fig. 11-5. Angular magnification.

However, in the case under consideration this reduces to

$$\beta' = c = \frac{1}{b} \qquad (11\text{-}8)$$

which, in a telescopic system, equals

$$\beta' = \frac{1}{\gamma} \qquad (11\text{-}9)$$

according to Eq. (11-7). This holds true for any given object distance and gives us an easy method to determine the angular magnification of a telescopic system.

It is clearly impossible to design a telescopic system consisting of a thin lens or thin system with a magnification other than $+1$ because for every thin system we have

$$b = c = +1$$

In order to get a magnified image we need a thick lens system or a system of separated thin lenses. In the most common cases we have the latter system. The simplest form will consist of two thin lenses separated by a distance t. Let us assume the components have powers a_1 and a_2. We then have

$$a_{1,2} = a_1 + a_2 - ta_1a_2$$
$$b_{1,2} = 1 - ta_2$$
$$c_{1,2} = 1 - ta_1$$

In order to be telescopic we have to make

$$a_{1,2} = 0$$

thus

$$t = \frac{a_1 + a_2}{a_1 a_2} = \frac{1}{a_2} + \frac{1}{a_1} = f_1' + f_2' \qquad (11\text{-}10)$$

With this value for t we find

$$b_{1,2} = 1 - \frac{a_1 + a_2}{a_1} = -\frac{a_2}{a_1} \tag{11-11}$$

$$c_{1,2} = 1 - \frac{a_1 + a_2}{a_2} = -\frac{a_1}{a_2} \tag{11-12}$$

To have a magnification >1 it is necessary to make

$$|a_2| > |a_1|$$

$$|f_2'| < |f_1'|$$

In order to have the images right side up, without the aid of extra lenses or prisms, we must make one of the lenses with a negative power. There is only one real solution because t can only be positive, thus a_2 is negative [see Eq. (11-10)]. In this way we arrive at the Gallilean telescope (Fig. 11-6).

It is easily seen that it is also possible to find a solution for a single thick lens this way. Here a_1 and a_2 represent the powers of the first and second surface. In our formulas the value t has to be reduced optically to t.

For many purposes the fact that the image is inverted is unimportant (astronomical telescopes, aiming telescopes), and we can

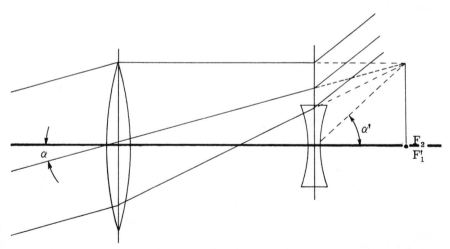

Fig. 11-6.   Gallilean telescope.

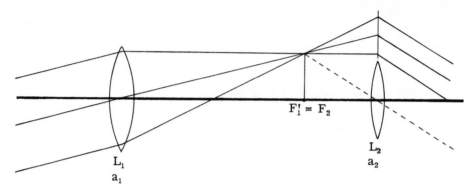

Fig. 11-7.   Inverting telescope.

find a solution with two positive thin lenses (Fig. 11-7).

In telescopes we have, besides the problem of correcting for aberrations, two very important quantities. The first one is the exit pupil of the instrument. In order to determine the exit pupil we have to find the entrance pupil. There are only two edges of lenses which can form the entrance pupil in this case. The first lens (objective) we do not have to image in the object space because the edge is already in the object space. The second lens (eyepiece), however, we do have to image back into object space. In doing so we have

$$\frac{1}{s'} = -\frac{a_1 a_2}{a_1 + a_2} + a_1$$

$$\frac{1}{s'} = \frac{a_1^2}{a_1 + a_2} \tag{11-13}$$

$$\frac{s'}{s} = \beta' = -\frac{a_1 + a_2}{a_1^2} \frac{a_1 a_2}{a_1 + a_2} = -\frac{a_2}{a_1} = \gamma$$

Thus we find that the diameter of this image is γ times larger than the diameter of the eyepiece. In practical telescopes the eyepiece always has a diameter large enough to make the objective the entrance pupil. Now we can image the edge of the objective in image space. The magnification factor is, according to Eq. (11-9), equal to $1/\gamma$. Actually the results of Eq. (11-13) could have been derived directly from Eq. (11-9), realizing that we image backward through the telescope. This relationship also gives us a sim-

ple way to find the magnification: by measuring the size of the exit
pupil and the objective.

It is customary to indicate on field glasses (binoculars) the angular magnification and the diameter of the objective. For instance, 6 × 30 means a magnification of 6 times and an objective
30 mm in diameter. According to the above, this means that the
exit pupil has a diameter of 5 mm. In ordinary daylight the pupil
of the eye is smaller than 5 mm, and the amount of light that the
eye can receive with this magnification is determined by the eye
and not by the telescope. However, under low light levels the eye
pupil enlarges and can become as large as approximately 8 mm.
Under these conditions we see that the instrument becomes the limiting factor as to the amount of light the eye receives. For this
reason, under such conditions it is better to use a 6 × 50 which has
an exit pupil of 8-1/3 mm, and again the eye is the limiting factor.

Not only is the diameter of the exit pupil important, its position is also important.

We find

$$\frac{1}{s'} = -\frac{a_1 a_2}{a_1 + a_2} + a_2 = \frac{a_2^2}{a_1 + a_2}$$

$$s' = \frac{1}{a_2}\frac{a_1}{a_2} + 1) = f_2'(1 - \frac{1}{\gamma})$$

For practical purposes this should not be smaller than 13 mm.
Given the magnification, this determines the smallest focal lengths
we can use.

In addition, the field of view is important. In the configuration
under consideration we have already seen that only two pupils exist.
The edge of the objective is the entrance pupil, thus the image of
the eyepiece is the field stop. We have already found that this was
imaged with a magnification γ. If the diameter of the eyepiece is
given by 2ϕ, the tan of the field angle is

$$\tan \alpha_1 = \frac{a_1 a_2 \phi}{a_1 + a_2} \tag{11-14}$$

It has already been shown that the field of view can be enlarged
by the use of field lenses. We could insert a field lens, for example, in the focal plane of the first lens. For color correction it is
then advantageous to give it the same power as the eyepiece lens.
We have already encountered this combination as a Ramsden eyepiece. If we give the field lens the same diameter 2ϕ, as the origi-

nal single eyepiece, we find for the field of view

$$\tan \alpha_2 = \frac{\phi}{f'} = a_1\phi \tag{11-15}$$

In comparing both cases we find

$$\frac{\tan \alpha_2}{\tan \alpha_1} = \frac{a_1\phi}{a_1a_2\phi}(a_1 + a_2) = (1 - \frac{1}{\gamma}) \tag{11-16}$$

Remembering that γ is a negative quantity we see that the field lens always increases the field of view.

In practice it is, of course, important to correct the aberrations in a telescope. For this reason the objective is usually a thin doublet. The eyepiece designs are very different for different telescopes, from Ramsden and Huygens eyepieces to much more complicated designs. An important consideration is also the angle in the image space (apparent field of view). If this becomes large it is more difficult to correct the eyepiece, and if it becomes greater than 60° we have to provide an exit pupil 25 mm behind the eyepiece. This makes the instrument large (see above), and special eyepiece designs are used to bring the exit pupil further away from the last surface.

For terrestrial use the image is often inverted by the use of Porro prisms which are shown in Fig. 11-8.

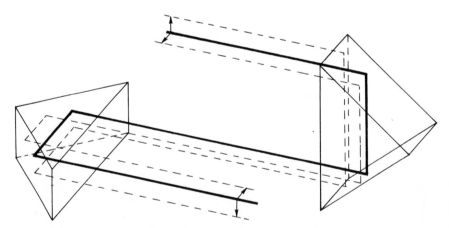

Fig. 11-8.   Porro prisms.

In binoculars it is very important that the optical axis of the two telescopes are parallel; otherwise the use of the instrument becomes very tiresome. This fault is difficult to detect without the use of special equipment.

PROBLEMS

Problem 1. Calculate the position of the exit pupil, the diameter of the exit pupil, and the field of view for the following system.

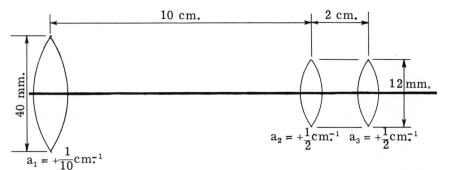

Example of a telescope

Problem 2. What forms the entrance pupil in a Gallilean telescope? What is the field stop? Derive an expression for the field of view.

OTHER FORMS OF TELESCOPES

Many astronomical telescopes make use of a mirror to form the primary image. A mirror has the advantage of being absolutely free from color aberrations. A spherical mirror has, however, the big disadvantage of having spherical aberration. To overcome this the spherical mirror is replaced by a parabolic one. The parabola has the property that all the light coming in parallel to the axis is focused in one point. For this point the imagery is thus perfect. The field of view, however, is very small because coma is worse for a parabolic mirror than for a spherical one. The usable field is in the order of not more than one degree.

Many forms of astronomical telescopes which make use of

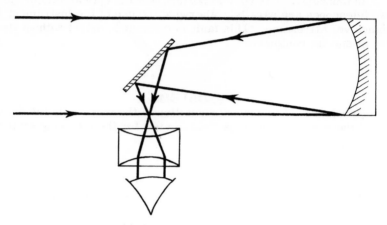

Fig. 11-9. Newtonian telescope.

mirrors are known. The most common one is the Newtonian telescope (Fig. 11-9). In order to see the image, a small 45° mirror
is used.

Another solution was introduced by Cassegrain (Fig. 11-10).
The secondary mirror in this system is used to form an enlarged
image behind the primary mirror, which has a hole in it through
which the rays pass. The primary mirror is again parabolic. The
secondary mirror is also aspheric to keep the axial image perfect
and is hyperbolic.

Secondary mirrors are always supported by some means, usually a "spider." These spiders give rise to diffraction patterns
with light peaks coming out of the center (Fig. 11-11).

In order to avoid this, Herschel suggested the off-axis solution

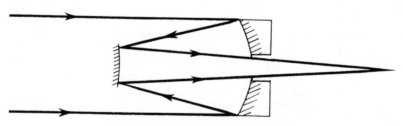

Fig. 11-10. Cassegrain telescope.

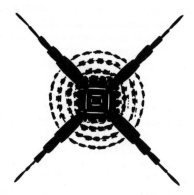

Fig. 11-11.   Diffraction pattern of a telescope with spider.

shown in Fig. 11-12.   This mirror is an off-axis piece of a much
larger parabolic mirror.   It is very expensive.

Recently many amateurs have been mounting secondary mirrors on a piece of plane-parallel optical glass.   This also serves
as a window to keep dirt off the primary mirror.   The disadvantage
of this solution is that the window must be of the same optical quality as the rest of the telescope, and for this reason is again expensive.

In order to increase the field of view of all telescopes with parabolic mirrors, Schmidt found a very ingenious solution.   He no-

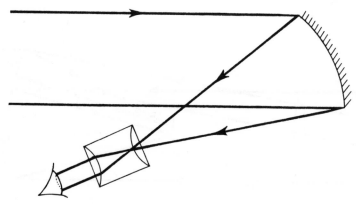

Fig. 11-12.   Herschel telescope.

ticed that the deformation of a flat round plate supported at the edge, and under uniform pressure, had the same equation as the deformation of a flat optical plate necessary to correct for the spherical aberration of a spherical mirror. He succeeded in actually fabricating these correction plates by putting plane-parallel optical plates on a round pipe and evacuating the air in the pipe. He then ground and polished the outside glass area flat again. When the pressure was released the newly polished surface assumed the correct aspheric surface. By putting the corrector plate in the center of curvature (Fig. 11-13), it acts in almost the same manner on all parallel bundles because in the first approximation the deviation of the rays is only a function of the wedge angle of the corrector plate. In this way the usable field of the optical system is tremendously increased to about 15°. This setup is usually used photographically. There is still one drawback. The field is not flat but spherical around the center of curvature of the primary mirror, which is easily seen from symmetry.

The fabrication of these corrector plates is very difficult. During World War II another solution was proposed independently by Maksutov in Russia and Bouwers in Holland. This used a spherical primary and corrector; however, all surfaces are concentric. Again, in this way, if the stop is located at this center of curvature, taking care of spherical aberration eliminates the aberrations over a wide field except for field curvature (Fig. 11-14).

For large aperture systems the corrector plate is often made of two pieces of glass of different dispersion but with the same mean refractive index to correct for the small color aberration introduced by this type of corrector.

This type of correcting system lends itself very well to the construction of telescopes as shown in Fig. 11-15.

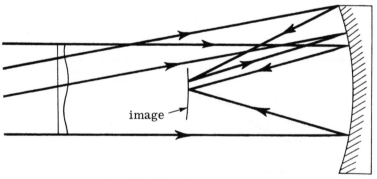

Fig. 11-13. Schmidt camera.

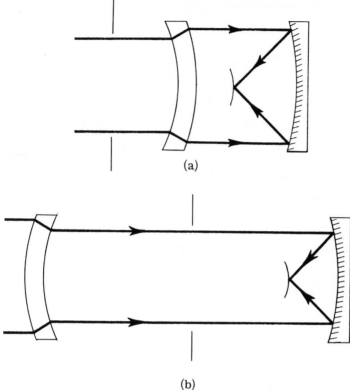

(a)

(b)

Fig. 11-14. Concentric systems.

THE SEXTANT

The sextant is an instrument used for measuring star positions (Fig. 11-16). A telescope (A) is mounted rigidly on frame (B). The half-silvered mirror (C) is mounted rigidly on the frame. Its position is such that the optical axis is reflected toward the mirror (D) mounted on arm (F) which can rotate around a point (E). The position of arm (F), and thus the angular position of mirror (D), can be read on the scale (G).

We aim the instrument in such a way that it points toward the horizon. The star in direction (I), whose elevation we want to find, is superimposed on the horizon by bringing the arm (F) with mirror (D) into the correct position.

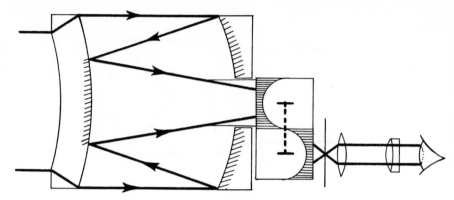

Fig. 11-15. Telescope with concentric objective.

We have redrawn the essential parts of the sextant in Fig. 11-17.

We want to find the elevation angle α between the horizon and the star. The angle β between the two mirrors is equal to the angle

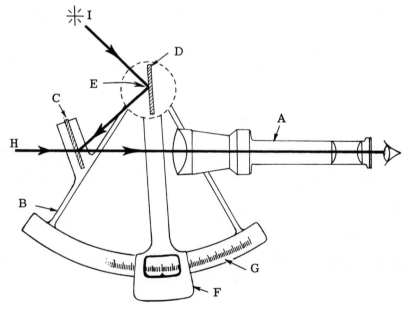

Fig. 11-16. Sextant.

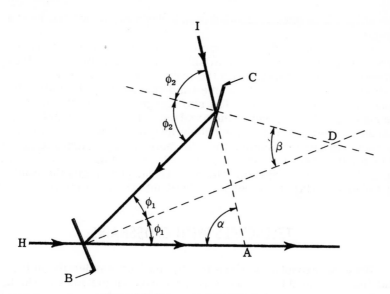

Fig. 11-17. Schematic sextant.

between the normals on the mirrors, and this angle can be read on scale (G). We want to find the relation between α and β. In triangle ABC we see that

$$2\phi_2 = \alpha + 2\phi_1$$

or

$$\alpha = 2(\phi_2 - \phi_1) \tag{11-17}$$

In triangle BDC we have

$$\phi_2 = \phi_1 + \beta$$

or

$$\beta = \phi_2 - \phi_1 \tag{11-18}$$

Combining Eq. (11-16) with Eq. (11-17) we have

$$\alpha = 2\beta$$

The scale (G) is usually divided in half degrees, so we can read α directly in degrees.

For airplane navigation a modification of the sextant is used. Here the horizon is often unavailable, and for this reason another reference is incorporated into the instrument. In most of these sextants this is an air bubble in a fluid chamber which is slightly dome shaped (Fig. 11-18). The star image is kept in the middle of the bubble. The motions of the airplane will move the bubble, and because of inertial effects the bubble may not always indicate the correct vertical. Assuming that the motions of the airplane are random, the resulting error can be reduced by taking several readings. Usually an integrator which continually averages the readings over a certain time period is built into the instrument.

TELESCOPES WITH CROSSHAIRS

If we put crosshairs in the focal plane of the objective in the real image formed by the objective, we have an instrument which, besides forming an enlarged image, can be used for many types of

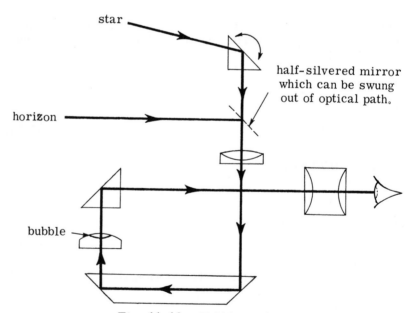

Fig. 11-18.   Bubble sextant.

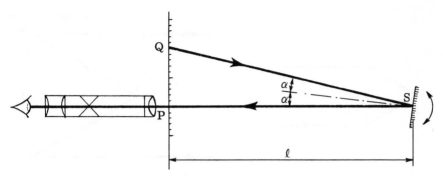

Fig. 11-19. Angle measurement with a telescope.

measuring. A commonly used laboratory technique of measuring the angular rotation of mirrors is shown in Fig. 11-19.

It is easily seen that

$$PQ = \ell \tan 2\alpha$$

For small angles we can replace this by

$$PQ = 2\ell\alpha$$

If, on the other hand, α becomes very large, the distance SQ changes enough to be troublesome. The scale then has to be made circular and must be made with the necessary precision.

If we mount the telescope in such a way that we can rotate it around both a vertical and horizontal axis while the amount of rotation can be read from circular scales, we have a theodolite (commonly called a transit). It is used for surveying purposes and can be used very successfully in many other measuring setups. In the more modern instruments the reading of the scales is done in the field of view of the telescope by means of a very ingenious optical design. The precision of these instruments is better than 1" of arc.

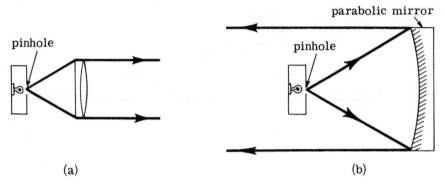

Fig. 11-20.   Collimators.

THE COLLIMATOR

There are various types of collimators. The simplest ones
are used to form parallel bundles of rays. These are shown in Fig.
11-20. The type shown in Fig. 11-20b is primarily used when a
parallel bundle with a large diameter is needed. The bundle
formed by the collimator, even if its objective is optically perfect,
is never precisely parallel because the pinhole must have a finite
size in order to let the light through. If d is the diameter of the
pinhole and f' the focal length of the lens, the maximum angle ϕ between the rays of the bundle (assuming a perfect objective) is

$$\phi = \frac{d}{f'} \tag{11-19}$$

Sometimes a slit is used instead of a pinhole. Another kind of collimator is used to put an image of some kind of target at infinity.
This target can be of any form. The most common ones are a cross
pattern. Sometimes a number of lines form the target. The line
spacing is chosen in such a way that the images subtend certain
given angles in the image space.

THE AUTOCOLLIMATOR

The collimator is often combined with a telescope, and it is
then called an autocollimator. There are many ways of accom-
plishing this.

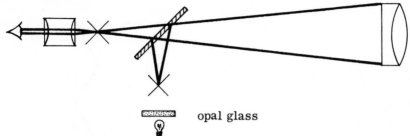

opal glass

Fig. 11-21. Autocollimator with half-silvered mirror.

Fig. 11-21 shows one form which uses a half-silvered mirror.

In Fig. 11-22 we have another solution. Here only part of the reticle is illuminated by means of a small prism.

Still another way of illuminating the reticle is shown in Fig. 11-23. Here the reticle is etched in a piece of highly polished plane-parallel glass. Light is introduced through the edge of the glass. Care must be taken to see that all the lightrays entering the glass are totally internally reflected. Only where the reticle is etched will the light escape.

Use of the Autocollimator

If we place a flat mirror in front of the autocollimator light will be reflected back into it. The autocollimator makes an image of the reticle at infinity. The flat mirror merely reverses the direction of the light and leaves the rays parallel. After reentering the instrument an image of the reticle is formed in the focal plane of the objective and can be viewed with the eyepiece. This gives us a good method for finding out whether or not two planes are paral-

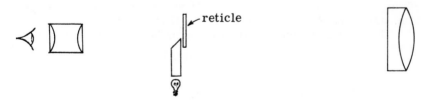

reticle

Fig. 11-22. Autocollimator with small prism for illumination.

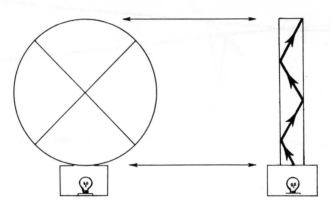

Fig. 11-23.   Internal reflection to illuminate a reticle.

lel to each other.   By placing the flat mirror on the front surface
we can locate the autocollimator in such a way that the image of the
reticle is formed on the crosshairs.   Then by placing the flat mirror on the second surface without moving the autocollimator, the
image should again be formed in the same place.

This principle can also be used to tell whether or not the ways
in a machine are straight.   If we place the flat mirror on a part
that moves over the ways under test and align the autocollimator,
we can move the mirror with the part it is connected to, over the
ways.   If the ways are straight, the reticle image will not move
with respect to the crosshairs.   For another simple way of testing
for straightness see the next chapter.

To test a plane-parallel plate for parallelism we simply put
the plate in front of the autocollimator.   If the two surfaces are
parallel we will have the two images, formed by the reflections of
the front and back surfaces, superimposed in the focal plane of the
objective.

The autocollimator is also very useful for the testing of 90°
prisms.   Let us first consider the case of two mirrors making a
90° angle with each other.   Let us follow a ray through such a system, assuming that the angle is 90° + ϵ (Fig. 11-24).

The angle ADC between the two normals on the mirror surfaces is

$$ADC = 90° - \epsilon$$

In triangle ACD we have

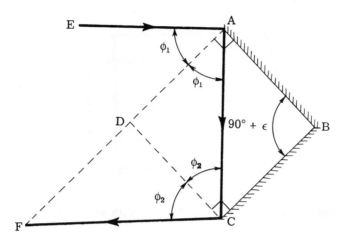

Fig. 11-24. Reflections in a 90° prism.

$$180° = 90° - \epsilon + \phi_1 + \phi_2$$

or

$$\phi_2 = 90° + \epsilon - \phi_1$$

The sum of the angles EAC and ACF is

$$2\phi_1 + 2\phi_2 = 2\phi_1 + 180 + 2\epsilon - 2\phi_1 = 180 + 2\epsilon \qquad (11\text{-}20)$$

We see that this is independent of ϕ_1 and, moreover, if $\epsilon = 0$ the incoming and outgoing rays are parallel.

   If we put this mirror system in front of an autocollimator as shown in Fig. 11-25, the upper part of the bundle will travel as indicated by arrow A while the lower part will travel as indicated by arrow B. If the angle α is exactly equal to 90°, the two returning halves of the bundle will be parallel and the two images in the focal plane will be superimposed. If, however, the angle α is $90 + \epsilon$, the two bundles will have an angle equal to 4ϵ between them and will form separate images in the focal plane of the objective. By putting an appropriate scale in this focal plane we have a simple way of measuring ϵ.

   If the two mirrors are part of a prism (Fig. 11-26) we must include the refraction of the rays at the entrance face.

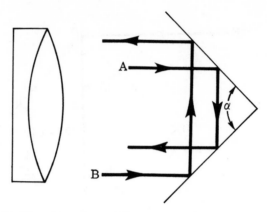

Fig. 11-25.   Testing a 90° angle with an autocollimator.

Supposing that the angle i is small, we have

$$\mu \, i_1' = i_1 \tag{11-21}$$

Inside the prism we again have the relation [Eq. (11-19)]. From this we determine

$$i_2 = i_1' - 2\epsilon \tag{11-22}$$

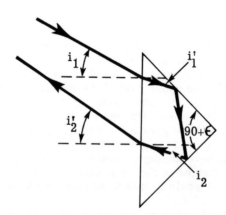

Fig. 11-26.   Rays passing through a 90° prism.

and again

$$i_2' = \mu i_2 \qquad (11-23)$$

Combining Eqs. (11-20), (11-21), and (11-22) we have

$$i_2' = \mu(i_1' - 2\epsilon) = i_1 - 2\mu\epsilon$$

or

$$i_2' - i_1 = 2\mu\epsilon \qquad (11-24)$$

In the autocollimator the images will be separated by an amount given by the angle $4\mu\epsilon$.

Aligning with the 'Young's Slits'

Professor Dr. A.C.S. Van Heel pointed out that Young's double slits could be used to align three points on a straight line. The advantages are the extreme simplicity combined with very high accuracy. In the setup shown in Fig. 11-27 we will see a set of colored bands in the eyepiece. The central band will be white and the others will have different colors. Some of these colored bands will

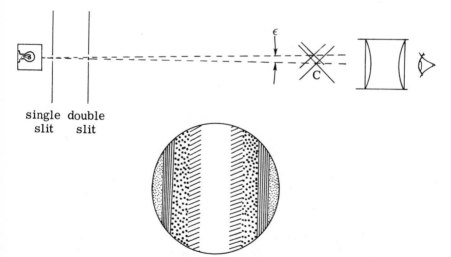

single double
slit   slit

Fig. 11-27.   Aligning with Young's slits.

have very sharp transitions.   The pattern will be symmetrical with respect to the central white band.   By measuring the position of two opposite sharp color transitions we can locate the center C behind them.   The single slit, the center of the double slit, and the point C will be located on a straight line.   The angular error ϵ (Fig. 11-27) can be kept to 1" of arc without elaborate equipment. This setup has been used to find deflections in buildings, bridges, etc.

It can easily be adapted to locate a line in space by replacing the single slit with a pinhole, the double slit with a set of concentric circular slits, and the crosshairs with a number of concentric circles etched on glass.   The setting here is done by symmetry. The same accuracy is achieved.

The Goniometer

The goniometer consists of an autocollimator mounted on a vertical axis.   The rotation of the autocollimator around this axis can be read on a graduated circle mounted below it.   Usually there is also a normal collimator, provided with an entrance slit, which can also be rotated around the same vertical axis (Fig. 11-28).

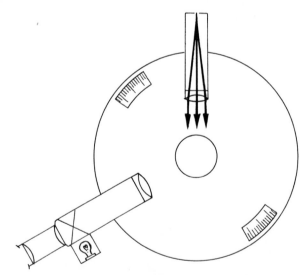

Fig. 11-28.   Goniometer.   (Note: The more precise instruments
                have provisions to read the scale on two opposite
                sides in order to eliminate the eccentricity of the
                scale.)

This instrument is mostly used to measure angles of prisms. For this purpose a small table is provided on the top of the axis, which has enough adjustments to bring it perpendicular to this axis. The measurement of a prism angle can be made in two ways.

With the Autocollimator Alone

Here we put the autocollimator perpendicular to one of the prism surfaces and a reading of the position α_1 of the autocollimator is made. Then the autocollimator is swung around and positioned perpendicular to the second surface and the position α_2 is read. Before the readings can be made we have to place the prism, with the help of the adjustments on the table, so that the two surfaces are parallel to the axis of rotation of the autocollimator (Fig. 11-29). From these readings we find

$$\gamma = \alpha_2 - \alpha_1$$

The angle β of the prism is then

$$\beta = 180 - \gamma = 180 - \alpha_2 + \alpha_1 \qquad (11\text{-}25)$$

With the Collimator

This is done as shown in Fig. 11-30. Again the two positions α_1 and α_2 are determined. The angle γ is given by

$$\gamma = 180 - \beta = i_1 + i_2$$

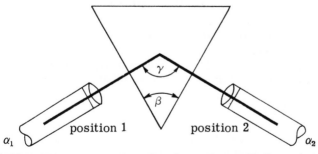

Fig. 11-29.   Measuring the angle of a prism with the autocollimator.

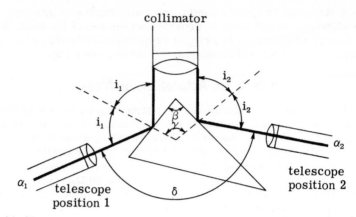

Fig. 11-30.   Measuring the angle or a prism with the goniometer.

and

$$\delta = \alpha_2 - \alpha_1 = 360 - 2i_1 - 2i_2$$

Combining the two equations

$$\delta = 2\beta \qquad\qquad\qquad (11\text{-}26)$$

The goniometer is also used to measure the refractive index of optical materials which will be dealt with in another chapter.

RANGEFINDERS

Rangefinders are used to measure distances. Many different principles are used.

Many military field glasses have a scale in the focal plane of the objective. From Fig. 11-31 we see that

$$AB = \frac{f'}{y}x$$

Usually the quantity f'/y is made 100. If we now know the size x of the object (plane, ship, etc.) we can estimate the distance AB.

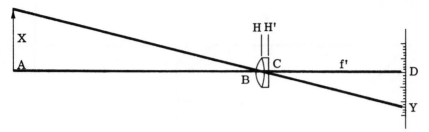

Fig. 11-31. Measuring the distance of objects of known dimensions.

In geodetic instruments use is often made of an idea shown in Fig. 11-32. In front of the objective of the telescope is mounted a prism covering half the aperture. The deviation through the prism is 0.01 radians. If we look at a stadia rod which is divided into inches, we will see two images of the scale on the rod. If the mark (b) of one of the scale images coincides with the 0 of the other image, the scale is 100 b inches away.

There are two types of rangefinders with which we can measure distance without knowing anything about the object.

Coincidence Rangefinder

The principle parts are shown in Fig. 11-33. Lightrays enter the two pentaprisms A_1 and A_2 and are deviated exactly 90°. The rays then enter the two objectives B_1 and B_2 and the

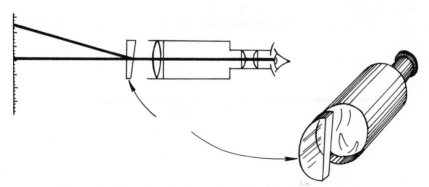

Fig. 11-32. Geodetic way of measuring distances.

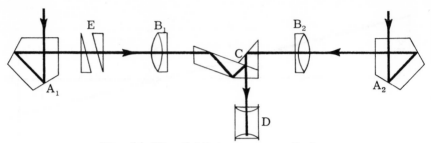

Fig. 11-33. Split-image rangefinder.

prism C, where the two bundles are combined through eyepiece D.
The prism C has different forms in instruments of different manufacturers. One form of it is shown in Fig. 11-34. The two parts
are cemented together along AB. Before cementing, however, the
left prism is aluminized along this surface. A rectangular portion
around C is left clear. All the bundles coming from the left side,
except those hitting this rectangular area, are reflected. The bundles coming from the right can only come through this clear area.
If this clear rectangle is in the focal plane of the objectives, the
image formed in this rectangle comes from the right objective B_2
while everything around it is made by the left objective B_1. If we
focus on an object at infinity, we will have one continuous image.
If, however, the object is not at infinity one image will be displaced with respect to the other. For this reason the prisms E are
incorporated. In the position shown the two prisms counteract each
other and act as a plane-parallel plate. If we rotate each through
the same angle around the optical axis of the system, but in opposite directions, it will deviate the bundle in one plane. This is
shown with the aid of a vector diagram in Fig. 11-35.

In the diagram we represent the deviations of the two prisms

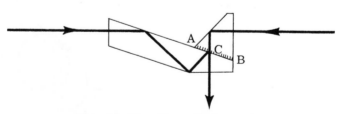

Fig. 11-34. Rangefinder prism.

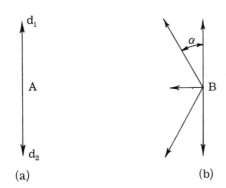

Fig. 11-35. Image displacement through double prism.

by d_1 and d_2. In Fig. 11-35 we represent the situation as shown in Fig. 11-33. No resultant deviation is produced. In Fig. 11-35b the prisms are rotated over an angle α according to the above description. We see that the resultant deviation δ is

$$\delta = 2d \sin \alpha \qquad\qquad (11-27)$$

By rotating the prisms until the two images superimpose, we can read the angle α and calculate the distance of the object. Usually the distance is directly marked on the drum moving the prisms. The precision with which distance can be measured is clearly a function of the base (distance between the two measuring beams) of the instruments.

There is another system to deviate the bundle. It is shown in Fig. 11-36. It consists of two lenses of equal and opposite power, a plano convex and a plano concave. The plane sides are placed together. Sliding one sideways causes a deviation of the beam.

Stereoscopic Rangefinders

Stereoscopic vision is a complicated mechanism. In principle it enables a person to judge distance by the fact that objects different distances away from the eyes do not form images in the same spots on the two retinas of the two eyes (Fig. 11-37). This relative change in position is interpreted by the brain as a change in distance. Suppose we use two eyepieces and put one in front of each eye. In the focal plane of the eyepieces we can put two identical scales. If they are lined up properly, they will form identical im-

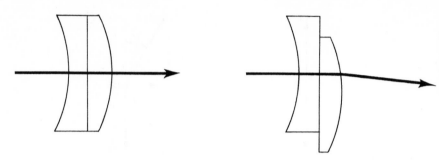

Fig. 11-36.   Deviation of a light bundle with a decentered lens.

ages on the same place on each retina. We can take one of the
lines of one of the scales and push it sideways. If we now look
through the eyepieces, this line and its companion will appear to
be a different distance away from the eye than in the first instance.
By doing this with many lines, each shifted over a different amount,
we can make the scale appear in space, one end closest to us and
the other farthest away. The stereo effect is directly related to
the distance between the eyes. The stereoscopic rangefinder is
shown in Fig. 11-38. The scales A are arranged in such a way
that they appear in the above-described way in space. At the same
time the distance between the objectives B and their focal length is
chosen in such a way that the images of an object formed at a given
distance will appear on the pair of lines which are marked for that
distance. The use of stereoscopic rangefinders is a job for which
the operator has to be trained.

Further study on this chapter is found in References 7, 11, 19,
22, 23, 39, 40, 52, 61, 79, 80, 83, 95, and 104.

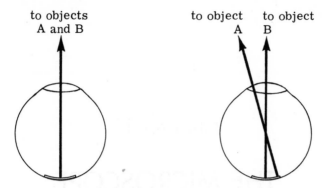

Fig. 11-37. Eye movement with changes in distance.

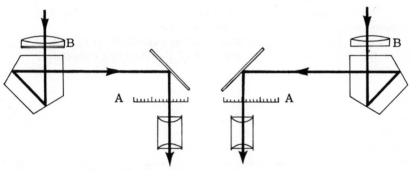

Fig. 11-38. Stereoscopic rangefinder.

Chapter 12

THE MICROSCOPE

The microscope is an instrument consisting of two optical components, an objective and an eyepiece.

Let us first investigate this system paraxially (Fig. 12-1). Here the objective and each element of the Huygens eyepiece is

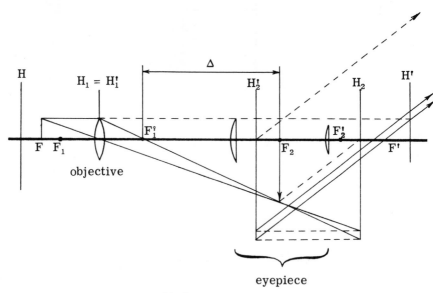

Fig. 12-1. The microscope.

considered to be thin.

The focal lengths of the objective and the eyepiece and the unit surfaces for each are given. From this we can construct the focal points and unit surfaces for the whole microscope. From the construction we see that the over-all power of the microscope has a negative value.

This is a visual instrument and again the magnification is defined as the loupe magnification [Eq. (11-1)] and is thus

$$V = \frac{25}{f} \qquad (12\text{-}1)$$

This can be rewritten in the following form:

$$\frac{1}{f} = a = a_1 + a_2 - da_1 a_2 = \frac{1}{f_1} + \frac{1}{f_2} - \frac{d}{f_1 f_2}$$

$$= -\frac{d - f_1 - f_2}{f_1 f_2} = -\frac{\Delta}{f_1 f_2} \qquad (12\text{-}2)$$

where

$$\Delta = d - f_1 - f_2 \qquad (12\text{-}3)$$

The distance Δ is standardized to 16 cm by the manufacturers of microscopes. With these relations we find

$$V = \frac{25\Delta}{f_1 f_2} = -\frac{16}{f_1} \frac{25}{f_2} \qquad (12\text{-}4)$$

The factor $16/f_1$ is usually called the magnification of the objective; the factor $25/f_2$ is called the magnification of the eyepiece.

To see the object we have to illuminate it. For transparent objects we use the light coming through them. For this purpose the microscope is supplied with a condenser system. For non-

transparent objects we have to supply a light source from the side
of the objective and use the reflected light to form the images.
The requirements of the illuminating system are determined by the
way the images are formed in the microscope and for this reason
we will discuss the various methods of the illumination later on.

The image formation in an optical instrument is determined by
several factors. We will investigate these in more detail in this
chapter because they play a very important role in the understanding of the practical limitations of a microscope.

Each point in the object is illuminated by bundles coming in different directions from the condenser system. Let us first simplify
the situation by assuming that only one flat wavefront is incident on
the object. In the object are regions which absorb light, others
which do not absorb light, and regions with differing refractive indices. All these differences will create diffracted light. This diffracted light will help form the image as far as it is passed by the
entrance pupil of the instrument. The entrance pupil, however, is
also an obstacle in the light path and causes further diffraction of
the light.

In reality we do not have just one wavefront illuminating the
object, but many wavefronts, each coming from different parts of
the light source. The sequence in which we consider the diffraction phenomena is immaterial.

Lord Rayleigh was the first one to investigate the light diffracted by the pupil. Each point in the object gives rise to the Airy
disc in the image plane. In this plane the diffraction patterns of
the different points in the object overlap. To arrive at the intensity distribution in the image plane due to the object we have to add
the diffraction patterns, taking into consideration the amplitudes
and phases.

Abbe pointed out that we could also start with the diffraction
pattern formed by the object (Franhofer diffraction). This is
formed in the focal plane of the objective. Not all the light diffracted by the object is passed by the objective. For this reason,
something less than the whole diffraction pattern formed by the object is imaged in the focal plane of the objective. From the light
distribution in the focal plane of the objective we can calculate the
intensity distribution in the image plane.

We will do this for a simplified case. As an object we will
take a grating with a grating constant p (Fig. 12-2). The light
from a plane incident wavefront, after passing the grating, will
have a maximum in the direction ϕ, if

$$\sin \phi = \frac{n\lambda}{p} \qquad\qquad\qquad (12\text{-}5)$$

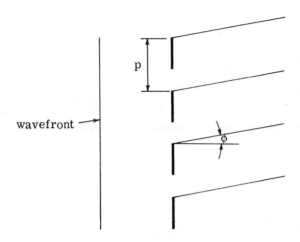

Fig. 12-2. A grating as an object for a microscope.

If we now put the objective in the diffracted light we get the situation shown in Fig. 12-3.

In the focal plane of the objective we shall image the diffraction pattern, which was formed at infinity, and thus have a number of diffraction maxima. The distance between these maxima is

$$q = f' \tan \phi \tag{12-6}$$

if the objective is in air. If we consider only small angles we can replace tan ϕ with sin ϕ and find with the help of Eq. (12-5):

$$q = f' \sin \phi = \frac{f'\lambda}{p} \tag{12-7}$$

These diffraction maxima are coherent. Shown here are only two maxima. It is clear, however, that many equidistant maxima are formed because of the relationship given in Eq. (12-5). We can consider these again as a new object forming the final image. It is clear that the light at Q is a maximum because AQ = EQ. To have a maximum at P we must have the condition

$$AP - BP = \lambda \tag{12-8}$$

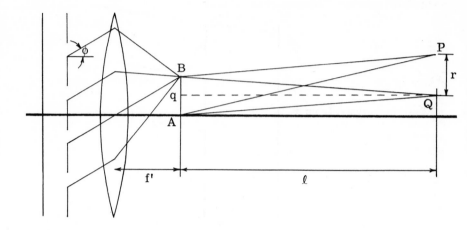

Fig. 12-3.   Image formation in a microscope with a grating in the
object space.

If the distance **PQ** equals r we have

$$AP - BP = \left\{(r + \tfrac{1}{2}q)^2 + \ell^2\right\}^{\frac{1}{2}} - \left\{(r - \tfrac{1}{2}q)^2 + \ell^2\right\}^{\frac{1}{2}}$$

or, expanding the square root into a power series:

$$r = \ell\left\{1 + \frac{1}{2}(\frac{r + \tfrac{1}{2}q}{\ell})^2\right\} - \ell\left\{1 + \frac{1}{2}(\frac{r - \tfrac{1}{2}q}{\ell})^2\right\}$$

$$= \frac{rq}{\ell} = \lambda \qquad \text{or} \qquad r = \frac{\ell\lambda}{q} \tag{12-9}$$

In combination with Eq. (12-7) we have

$$r = \frac{\ell p}{f'} \tag{12-10}$$

Here again we have many equidistant maxima. We see that this is
independent of the wavelength. We shall see this series of maxima

for every distance ℓ. The actual image is formed when the distance ℓ equals Δ. Then we have

$$r = \frac{\Delta}{f'}p \qquad\qquad (12\text{-}11)$$

which is the correct distance r because if Δ is large compared to f', the object is placed practically in the object focal point of the objective, and the magnification is equal to $-\Delta/f'$. (The small difference here is due to all the approximations made throughout the derivation.) It seems that it is impossible to find the actual image plane. This, however, changes when we take incident wavefronts, falling under different directions on the object, into account. If the incident wavefront is not perpendicular to the axis, the diffraction maxima in the objective focal plane are again the same distance apart, but they are, however, laterally displaced compared to those formed by a wavefront entering under a different angle. The only plane where all these maxima "line up" is the image plane. This can be understood by realizing that the optical path length for each ray, from object to image point, is the same. In this plane it is thus immaterial where, in the object focal plane, the maxima for all the incoming wavefronts were located.

To form an image of the grating it is thus necessary to have at least two maxima formed in the focal plane of the objective. The angle U, accepted by the objective, should thus be at least

$$\sin U = \frac{\lambda}{p} \qquad\qquad (12\text{-}12)$$

The medium between the object and the objective can have a refractive index μ (immersion objectives). In this case the wavelength λ_0 in air is related to the wavelength in the medium by

$$\lambda = \frac{\lambda_0}{\mu} \qquad\qquad (12\text{-}13)$$

and for Eq. (12-12) we find

$$\sin U = \frac{\lambda_0}{\mu p} \qquad\qquad (12\text{-}14)$$

Thus, the smallest detail we can see is given by

$$p = \frac{\lambda_0}{\mu \sin U} = \frac{\lambda_0}{A} \qquad\qquad (12\text{-}15)$$

where A is the numerical aperture of the objective.

The same results would be obtained if Lord Rayleigh's way of treating the image formation were followed. Mathematically this is more difficult.

The foregoing treatment shows a way to increase the resolving power. If the illuminating bundle makes an angle with the optical axis in such a way that only two diffraction maxima are formed in the focal plane of the objective, we still see detail, and the size of the detail visible is half the value found in Eq. (12-15) (Fig. 12-4).

In the above treatment we assumed that the illumination of the object was done by plane wavefronts, in other words, with coherent light. What would happen if the light were completely incoherent, or in other words, self-emitting? The image of a point A (Fig. 12-5a) is formed at A'. We shall assume a rectangular lens. This however is a $\sin x/x$ intensity pattern, as shown in Fig. 12-5b. The first zero in this pattern is found by realizing that the light intensity at x_0 is determined by adding up all the contributions of each part of the wavefront with the right phase. The phase difference between the light from different portions of the wavefront is equal to the difference between the wavefront and a reference sphere with x_0 as its center. One such reference sphere is shown in Fig. 12-5a. In a first approximation this phase difference is a linear variation going from one end (zero) to the other end of the wavefront (maximum PQ).

We could divide the wavefront into a number of small equal

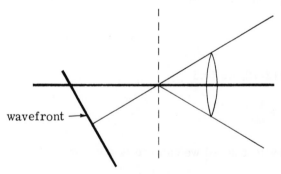

Fig. 12-4. Oblique illumination.

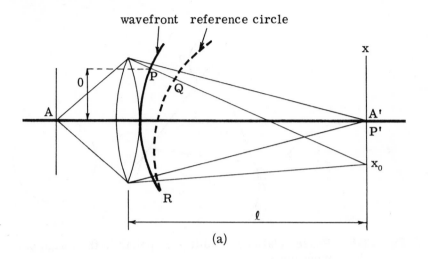

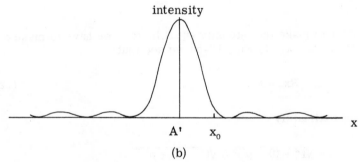

(b)

Fig. 12-5. (a) Diffraction in the image space. (b) Intensity pattern for a rectangular aperture.

areas and give each area an average phase and intensity. The intensity in x_0 could then be found by adding the contributions of each small area as vectors as shown in Fig. 12-6a.

By making each area smaller and smaller we would decrease the intensity of each area and make the phase difference between successive areas smaller and smaller. In the limit it would approach the arc of a circle in our vector diagram (Fig. 12-6c). The angle α represents the phase difference and is equal to

$$\alpha = \frac{PQ}{\lambda} 2\pi \qquad (12\text{-}16)$$

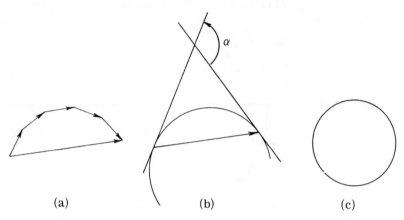

(a)   (b)   (c)

Fig. 12-6.   Phase relations for different points in the image of a
point object.

In order to make the intensity equal to zero we have to make $\alpha = 2\pi$
and thus $PQ = \lambda$.   In Fig. 12-5a we see that

$$Px_0 - Rx_0 = \lambda \tag{12-17}$$

Or approximately

$$\lambda = \sqrt{\ell^2 + (0 + p')^2} - \sqrt{\ell^2 + (0 - p')^2}$$
$$= 2\frac{0p'}{\ell}$$

or

$$p' = \frac{\lambda \ell}{2 \cdot 0} \tag{12-18}$$

In general we assume that the images of two points can be recog-
nized as such if these images are not closer together than when the
maximum of one falls on the first minimum of the other, as shown
in Fig. 12-7 (Rayleigh criterion).   In our case a distance p' apart.
This corresponds to two object points a distance p apart where

$$p = \frac{p'}{\beta'} \approx \frac{p'}{\dfrac{\Delta}{f'}} \tag{12-19}$$

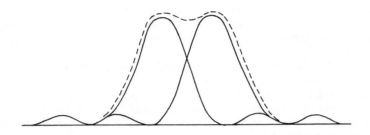

Fig. 12-7. Two-point resolution.

Combining this with Eq. (12-18) and again assuming that $\Delta \approx \ell$ we find

$$p = \frac{1}{2}\lambda\frac{f'}{0} \tag{12-20}$$

For purposes of simplicity we have taken a square aperture and other approximations. If we had started with a round aperture we would have found

$$p = \frac{1}{2}\frac{\lambda}{\sin U} \tag{12-21}$$

Again introducing λ_0 for the wavelength in vacuum for the case $\mu \neq 1$ we find

$$p = \frac{1}{2}\frac{\lambda_0}{\mu \sin U} = \frac{1}{2}\frac{\lambda_0}{A} \tag{12-22}$$

For the derivation of the above results without all the approximations, see Professor E. L. O'Neill's course in "Selected Topics in Optics and Communication Theory."

From the above we see that there is a difference of a factor of two, in resolving power, between coherent and incoherent illumination. What form of illumination do we actually have in a microscope? If the light source is imaged by the condenser in the object it depends on the aperture of the condenser. If the aperture is small, the Airy disc in the image of each point of the source is large and they overlap considerably. In this case we have practi-

cally complete coherent illumination. The larger the aperture of
the condenser, the smaller the Airy disc of each image point of the
source, and the less coherent the illumination becomes. So we
come to the practical rules for the condenser aperture and illumination.

For a grating type structure in the object, the best illumination
is that shown in Fig. 12-4. For irregular small detail we should
use as large an aperture as possible. This, however, increases
the amount of stray light considerably and "drowns" detail out. A
practical compromise is a condenser aperture of about 1/3 that of
the objective aperture.

From the previous discussions it follows that it is advantageous to make $\mu \sin U$ as large as possible. There are two variables with which to accomplish this: μ and U.

To make U as large as possible, we often make use of the
aplanatic points. To increase μ we immerse the object in a fluid
with a refractive index larger than the refractive index of air.
Such an objective is called an "immersion objective." In this way
one can realize a numerical aperture of 1.3. For small values of
A ordinary dry objectives are used. Two forms of microscope objectives are shown in Fig. 12-8. Microscope objectives have very
small fields and are very highly corrected on axis. Chromatic aberrations are corrected by the use of properly selected glasses and
power distributions. The magnification varies also with wavelength.

Apochromatic objectives are objectives in which the color is
corrected for three wavelengths and the axial imagery is aplanatic
for two wavelengths. To achieve this superior color correction, it

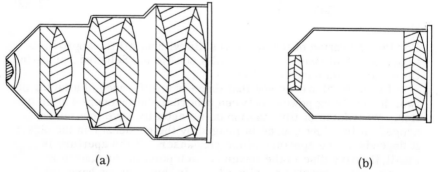

(a)   (b)

Fig. 12-8.   (a) Immersion objective.   (b) Dry objective.

is necessary to use fluorite as one of the components.

It is also clear that because the resolving power is limited, there does exist a magnification beyond which we shall not see more detail. The maximum useful magnification is related to the resolving power of the eye. We have stated that the eye can resolve details if they have an angular separation of 1'. To make sure that we do not lose detail, let us make the smallest detail subtend an angle of 3'. We have found that

$$V = \frac{\tan \alpha'}{\tan \alpha} = \frac{\tan \alpha'}{\dfrac{p}{25}}$$

and

$$p = \frac{1}{2} \frac{\lambda_0}{A}$$

Making $\tan \alpha'$ equal $\tan 3' = 0.009$ and using

$$\lambda_0 = 0.5 \times 10^{-4} \text{cm},$$

$$V = \frac{0.0009 \times 25}{0.5 \times 5 \times 10^{-4}} A \approx 1000 \, A$$

Magnifying beyond this will not show more detail, but will result in loss of light.

The depth of field of microscopes is very small, especially for large values of A. We can find the order of magnitude of this depth of field in the following way (Fig. 12-9).

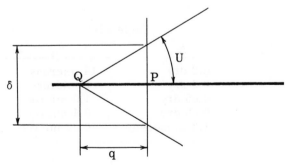

Fig. 12-9. The depth of focus of a microscope.

Suppose the microscope is focused at point P. Point Q, a distance q away from P, will look like an area with diameter δ.

$$\frac{\frac{1}{2}\delta}{q} = \tan U \qquad (12\text{-}23)$$

It is clear that we could have taken Q on the other side of P. The total depth will thus be proportional to 2q. The tolerable size of δ will be related to the smallest detail one can see; in other words, between $1/2\ \lambda_0/A$ and λ_0/A. If we take the last value we find

$$2q = \frac{\delta}{\tan U} = \frac{\lambda_0}{A \tan U} = \frac{\lambda_0 \cos U}{A \sin U} \qquad (12\text{-}24)$$

We know that

$$\sin U = \frac{A}{\mu}$$

Thus

$$2q = \frac{\lambda_0 \sqrt{1 - \dfrac{A^2}{\mu^2}}}{\dfrac{A^2}{\mu}} \qquad (12\text{-}25)$$

Taking $\lambda_0 = 0.56$ micron we find Table 12-1. Sometimes this extremely small value for the depth of field can be very useful (com-

Table 12-1

A	2q
0.2 dry	14 microns
0.3 dry	6 microns
0.65 dry	1.0 micron
0.85 dry	0.4 micron
1.3 immersion	0.26 micron

Table 12-2

V_{obj}	d
8	9 mm
10	7 mm
40	0.6 mm
90	0.2 mm

paring Johansson blocks etc.).

Another important value is the free object distance, which is the distance between the object and the first surface of the objective. Table 12-2 gives some average values of this value d as a function of the magnification V_{obj} of the objective.

To illuminate the object a condenser is used. It is used to increase the illumination level in the image, which can become very low at high magnifications. It also makes it possible to control the mode of illumination (coherent or incoherent). For this reason it is advantageous to be able to make the aperture of the illuminating bundle equal to the aperture of the objective used. In order to change the aperture of the condenser at will, a diaphragm is incorporated. This diaphragm can, in good microscopes, be placed eccentric to the axis to accomplish oblique illumination. To minimize the stray light in the final image it is advantageous to illuminate only that area of the object of which an image is formed in the microscope. For this purpose a second diaphragm is provided between the light source and the condenser. This diaphragm is imaged by the condenser in the object plane.

For viewing opaque objects a special type of microscope is used. Here we must illuminate the object through the objective with a vertical illuminator, as shown in Fig. 12-10.

For the comfort of the observer some microscopes are provided with two eyepieces. These are known as binocular microscopes. Most of them have only one objective, and a beam splitter is used to divide the bundle and present an image to both eyes. These microscopes have no stereoscopic vision. With lower magnifications it is possible to build true stereoscopic microscopes, the axes of which are inclined in such a way that each focuses on the same object and the occulars are the proper eye distance apart.

Measuring microscopes have graduated scales in the image plane of the objective, or, are provided with crosshairs. The whole microscope is mounted in a frame which can be moved with the aid of a screw. With such a microscope length measurements can be made.

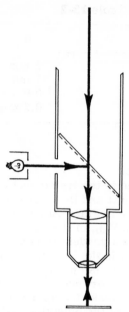

Fig. 12-10.   Microscope for opaque objects.

OTHER TYPES OF MICROSCOPES

Dark Field Illumination

Although the previously described limit for resolving small
detail is valid, it is possible to see whether or not particles which
are smaller than indicated by this limit are present in the field of
view. If a particle smaller than the above limit is in the field, it
will scatter light but no real image will be formed. If, however,
no direct light enters the objective we will see a dark field. If
there are small particles in the field of view, we could have diffracted light coming from these particles and entering the objective. In this way we shall see light coming from the point where
the particle is located. We cannot see detail or size, however. A
way of doing this is shown in Fig. 12-11.

Phase Objects

Until now we have been talking about objects which could be
described as objects having varying transmissions. There are,

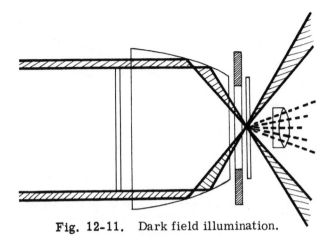

Fig. 12-11.   Dark field illumination.

however, many objects (for example, many living tissues) which
have detail as far as a variation in refractive index goes, but which
are completely transparent.   These so-called phase objects are
practically invisible in a normal microscope.   The reason is that,
although an image is formed, each point has the same intensity and
the only difference is the phase of the light in the different portions
of the image.   This phase difference is introduced by the refractive
index differences if we illuminate the object with coherent light.
This, however, the eye or photographic plate cannot see because
all physical detectors will detect only amplitude differences and not
phase differences as such.   To see an object like this we have to
introduce special techniques.

Interference Microscopes

We will assume that the optics in the microscope are perfect,
that is to say, the phase distribution in the image is the same as
the phase distribution in the object.

If the incident light is coherent, the phases in the image will
be completely determined by the refractive indices in the object,
assuming this to be only a phase object.   Suppose we have phase
variations for a few different points in an image as shown in Fig.
12-12 by dashed lines. Notice that these are all equally long because no absorption was assumed.   Let us now add to each of these
a wave with a certain amplitude and phase as indicated by the thin
vectors which again all have the same length.   The resultant amplitude in each point is then shown by the heavy vector.   We

Fig. 12-12. Phase relations in the interference microscope.

see that the resultants are now different in length. If we could add
vectors like these in the real image we could make these index
variations visible as intensity variations.

Before showing how this can be done we will describe this in a
slightly different manner. If the only differences are phase variations, the points in the image can be represented by vectors in different directions but all equally long. If we draw them all from
one point, all the ends of the vectors will be on a circle as shown
in Fig. 12-13, in which two vectors A and B are shown. Drawing
the vectors is quite unnecessary. Just giving the points C and D is
sufficient to define the phases. Adding the constant light vector is

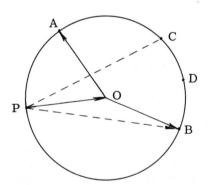

Fig. 12-13. Vector diagram representing the phase in a phase
object.

now easy because only one vector has to be drawn.   Let us choose,
for instance, PO.   The amplitude in point B is now the vector PB
and in point C, it is PC.   We see that adding the constant vector
simply changes the origin from O to P.

To realize this several setups are used.   One is shown in Fig.
12-14.

The incident wavefront is split into two bundles by the half-
silvered mirror A.   In one of the beams the object is inserted.
Identical objectives are inserted into both bundles and then the two
bundles are recombined as shown.

An ingenious solution by Dyson is shown in Fig. 12-15.   The
object is placed between two plates A and B.   These plates are
each half-silvered on both sides.   Note that one plate has a fully
aluminized spot to prevent the direct light from reaching the objective.   The light path is shown in the figure.   Again we have a beam
passed to the object and one which did not pass to the object, which
are recombined.

Another solution is given by F. H. Smith.   A birefringent plate
is inserted between the object and the condenser.   A cone of light
is now divided into two beams and focused in two different points A
and B (Fig. 12-16).   The object is now placed in one of these
points, say A.   Afterwards the light again goes through an identical
birefringent plate in such a way that the images of A and B again
coincide.   All the light going through A is shifted in phase according to the value of the refractive index at A.   The light going

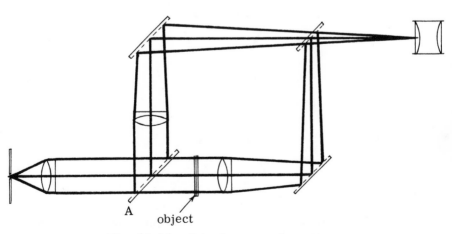

Fig. 12-14.   Interference microscope.

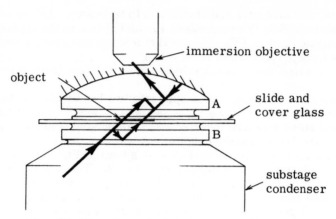

Fig. 12-15. Dyson's interference microscope.

through B will have the average phase of the surroundings of A. If the areas with different refractive indices are small in size, the phase of the two bundles will be different and again the two beams will interfere. This setup is particularly useful if the average refractive index does not change for different areas in the object.

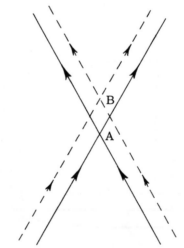

Fig. 12-16. Light paths in an interference microscope with birefringent plate.

Phase Microscopes

For objects with small phase variations the points representing the image in a vector diagram are all close together on the arc of the circle (Fig. 12-17). From the Abbe theory of image formation we see that we have in the focal plane of the objective, a series of bright spots. The central one would be there even if there were no object at all and is called the direct light. Suppose this light is given by the vector P. It is also shown that if this were the only light passed by the objective we would see an equally illuminated image field. If we have a phase object as represented in Fig. 12-17 we will still have this central maximum in the object focal plane. The intensity will now be the average of all the vectors and could be the vector ON. The amplitude of the light in that point of the image represented, for instance by B, can be thought of as the result of two waves, one with an amplitude and phase represented by ON and the other represented by NB. Now by placing an obstacle in the central maximum to prevent this direct light from reaching the image plane, we would alter the intensity distribution in this image plane profoundly. It is easily seen that the intensities are now given in our diagram by taking N as the origin. This is the so-called Schlieren method by Toepler. It can also be seen that this system has drawbacks. The points at A and B will have the same intensities. Now these points do have different phases. Let us now suppose that B is lagging in phase as compared to A. An ingenious solution was proposed by Zernike to see these phase differences all in the right order. Suppose we place in the central maximum, not an opaque obstacle but a transparent obstacle, such

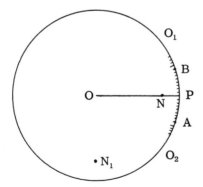

Fig. 12-17.   Vector diagram for objects with small phase variations.

as to bring the phase of this light ahead by a factor of $\pi/2$. This is the same as taking the vector ON away and then adding a vector ON_1. To get the intensities in the image we have to add to the vectors NA, NB, etc., the vector ON_1. This, however, is the same as bringing the origin in the point O_1 where O_1N equals ON_1. Now we see clearly that the vectors O_1B and O_1A have different lengths. This is called positive phase contrast. We could also have retarded the direct light by a factor of $\pi/2$. Then the result is given by placing the origin in O_2, and this is called negative phase contrast.

Usually the obstacle, called the phase plate, besides changing the phase by a factor of $\pi/2$, also absorbs some of the light and shortens the vector. The reason is that we are often interested in very small phase differences, and all the image points lay very close together on the arc of the circle (Fig. 12-18). Instead of bringing the origin at O_1, which would give poor contrast in the image (all resultant vectors are approximately equally long), we now bring the origin in O_1'. In other words, part of the direct light is absorbed and the difference in the length of the vectors for different image points is relatively increased and, thus also, the contrast in the image.

It should again be realized that the above description is very incomplete and only tries to give a physical picture of what is going on. For a complete description we again have to refer to the literature.

The setup for Schlieren observations is shown in Fig. 12-19.

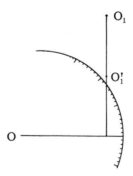

Fig. 12-18. Vector diagram showing the influence of the phase
            plate.

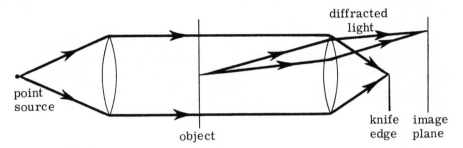

Fig. 12-19. Knife edge image.

This setup can be greatly simplified as shown in Fig. 12-20. The object here is viewed directly with the eye.

Instead of using a point source in phase contrast, an annular aperture is often used as a source to get more light in the final image. In this case the phase plate also has an annular form. The setup is shown in Fig. 12-21.

For further information see References 1, 4, 5, 7, 10, 33, 59, 61, 78, 80, and 103.

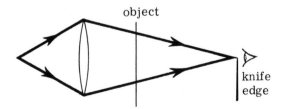

Fig. 12-20. Knife edge test.

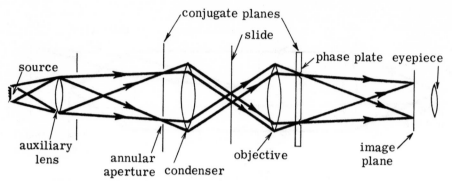

Fig. 12-21. Phase microscope with annular phase plate.

PROBLEM
Construct the path for real rays in a microscope, assuming again that all the individual lenses are thin.

Chapter 13

OTHER OPTICAL INSTRUMENTS

CAMERAS

The principle parts of a camera are: (1) camera body, (2) lens, (3) shutter, (4) film transport mechanism, (5) focusing device, (6) viewer.

The Camera Body

The camera body should be sturdy enough so that the camera lens can be accurately brought into focus, with no vibration being transported through the body when the shutter is released.

The Lens

The angular field of view of the lens has to be large enough so that it will cover the whole photographic plate. The relation between the field angle 2ω and the size of the photographic plate is given by

$$\tan \omega = \frac{a}{s' - s'_p} \qquad (13\text{-}1)$$

(See Fig. 13-1.)

For most photographic lenses the exit pupil is located in or very near the image unit plane and in this case we have

$$\tan \omega = \frac{a}{f'} \qquad (13\text{-}2)$$

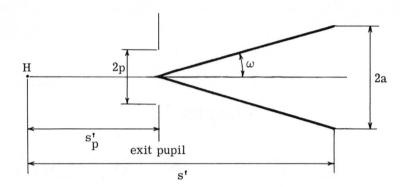

Fig. 13-1. Principal quantities determining the exposure through a lens.

The F number determines the necessary exposure time. This has been discussed in Chap. 5.

The correction of aberrations in photographic objectives is difficult because in most cases the F number is small while the field of view is relatively large. This means that all aberrations have to be corrected.

It is often important to know just how large a certain detail will be when imaged on the negative. If the detail size is too small, it may not be possible to recognize it because the photographic material is not perfect but has grain. For this reason long focal-length lenses are often used. These are apt to make the camera unwieldy; instead we prefer to use telephoto objectives. In these lenses ℓ_F' is much smaller than f'. The simplest form of a telephoto lens is the combination of a positive lens and a negative one. The power of this is given by

$$a_{1,2} = a_1 + a_2 - ta_1a_2 \tag{13-3}$$

where t is the distance between the two lenses, each of which is considered thin. The focal length will be taken to be +1. Thus Eq. (13-3) becomes

$$1 = a_1 + a_2 - ta_1a_2 \tag{13-4}$$

If we now introduce

$$a_2 = -ma_1$$

we find for t,

$$t = \frac{1 - a_1 + ma_1}{ma_1^2} \tag{13-5}$$

In order to have the shortest-length camera, we must make the distance from the first lens to the focal plane p as short as possible (Fig. 13-2). Now

$$p = \ell'_H + f' + t$$

$$= C + t = 1 - ta_1 + t$$

With Eq. (13-5) we find

$$p = 1 - \frac{1 - a_1 + ma_1}{ma_1} + \frac{1 - a_1 + ma_1}{ma_1^2}$$

$$= -\frac{2}{ma_1} + \frac{1}{m} + \frac{1}{ma_1^2} + \frac{1}{a_1}$$

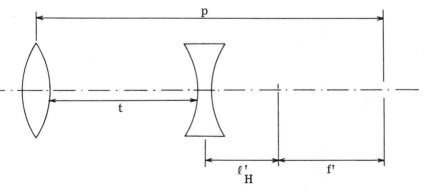

Fig. 13-2. Principle of a telephoto lens.

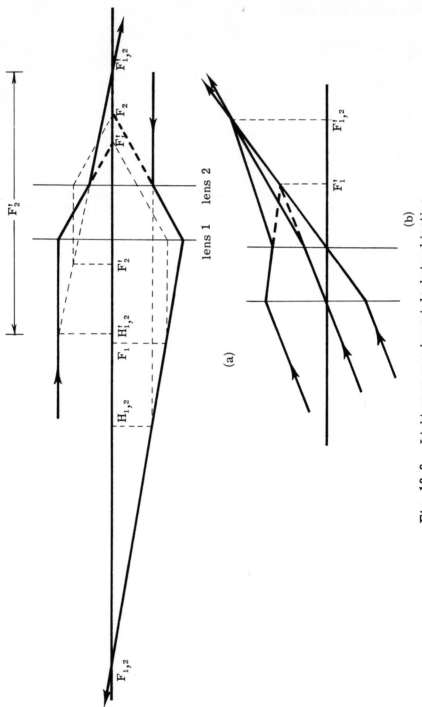

Fig. 13-3. Light rays passing a telephoto objective.

To make p a minimum

$$\frac{dp}{da_1} = \frac{2}{ma_1^2} - \frac{2}{ma_1^3} - \frac{1}{a_1^2} = 0$$

or

$$a_1 = \frac{2}{2 - m} \qquad\qquad (13\text{-}6)$$

Thus from Eq. (13-5) we determine

$$t = \frac{2 - m}{4} \qquad\qquad (13\text{-}7)$$

and

$$\ell_F' = 0.5 \qquad\qquad (13\text{-}8)$$

This is the shortest telephoto combination one can make with two thin components. In Fig. 13-3, we show the construction of the principle points for such a system and also the paraxial construction for an off-axis bundle.

Sometimes it is necessary to cover an extremely large angular field. This is done with a wide-angle lens. A very simple form which covers a 180° field is shown in Fig. 13-4. One has to realize that distortion must be introduced to image this field of view on a flat piece of film.

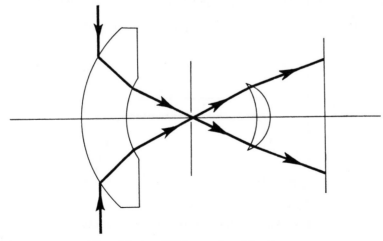

Fig. 13-4. Wide-angle objectives.

Shutters

There are two widely used types of shutters: (a) Between-the-lens shutter. Here the shutter is usually located very close to the aperture stop and consists of a number of thin blades which move away from each other and close again. (b) Focal-plane shutter. Here a screen with a slit in it is moved laterally just in front of the film. The exposure takes place during the time that the slit passes the light to the film.

The two types of shutters have completely different properties. The between-the-lens shutter takes a finite time to open complete-ly, but each point in the image gets the light at the same time and in the same amount. It also takes a finite time for the shutter to close. See the dotted line in Fig. 13-5.

With the focal-plane shutter, the time of exposure of each point in the image depends on where it is located. Suppose the slit moves from left to right; then the portions on the left in the image are exposed before the portions on the right. Usually the speed of the screen is a constant while the different exposure times are ac-complished by changing the slit width. This is not so on all cam-eras. Sometimes both slit width and screen speed can be changed. By bringing the screen very close to the film each point gets the full illumination almost from the beginning to the end of the expo-sure, and the exposure can be made approximately as shown by the thin line in Fig. 13-5. This is the shortest time span to get the full exposure. To get the same exposure with a between-the-lens shutter, we need a longer time. The exposure time for the image as a whole is much longer with the focal-plane shutter. This gives rise to the well-known effect where pictures of racing cars show the cars shortened or lengthened or the top as being fur-ther ahead than the bottom, depending on which way the slit was moving.

The efficiency E of the shutter is generally defined as

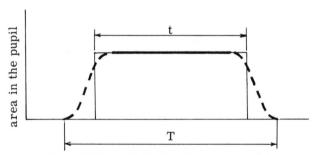

Fig. 13-5. Light flux through a shutter.

$$E = t/T$$

(See Fig. 13-5.)

The focal-plane shutter has a big advantage in that it is much easier to make the lenses interchangeable because the shutter is in no way connected with the lens.

Film-Transport Mechanism

The biggest problem here is to move the film and, after the movement, have the film precisely located again in the focal plane without scratching the film. In large cameras the pressure plate that holds the film in the focal plane is, therefore, sometimes released before the film is transported.

In most modern amateur cameras the film transport is coupled with the shutter in such a way that, while transporting the film, the shutter is also wound for the next exposure.

Focusing Devices

Here a wide variety is used and we will only mention the most common types.

a. Ground glass. Here the image is focused on a piece of ground glass. It is either inserted in the place of the film, or a mirror is inserted between the lens and the film to deviate the bundles toward the ground glass. Before exposure the mirror is moved out of the way. This last solution is much faster in use than the first one. The use of ground glass is a very simple solution if one wants to interchange lenses.

b. Coupled rangefinders. Here a small split-field rangefinder is built onto the camera. By moving the focusing knob one focuses the lens and simultaneously moves one of the mirrors of the rangefinder (Fig. 13-6).

It is fairly difficult to make interchangeable lens cameras of this type, but it is done in some of the more expensive models. Many more refinements are used but are beyond the scope of this course.

Viewers

The simplest form is a wire frame of the right size and distance from the eye. The eye sees the frame at the same time as the scene. If a ground glass is incorporated, there is, of course, no real need for another viewer although, for the sake of convenience, one of the other types is often also incorporated.

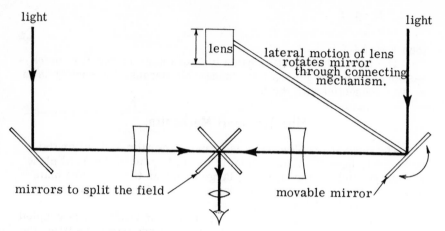

Fig. 13-6.   Rangefinder for a camera.

An optical type of viewer is also often used. This consists of a Gallilean telescope used backward, that is to say, it demagnifies. The positive lens is the field stop, and by giving it the right shape one can only see that part of the object which will be imaged by the camera.

One of the things which gives rise to difficulties is "parallax," caused by the fact that the viewer and the camera lens cannot be located in the same place. If the object is far away, the difference between what one sees through the viewer and what is photographed is very small compared to the field photographed. If one comes closer, however, it can become significant (Fig. 13-7).

In some cameras there are provisions for correcting for parallax.

PROJECTORS

We shall first discuss the projection of transparent objects such as slides and films.

Figure 13-8 shows what the result would be if one tries to project object A with lens L by placing the source B behind A. Only a small area CD would be illuminated. Furthermore, only a small portion of the lens L is filled with "direct light."

If we bring B closer to A we can increase the illumination of the screen because we utilize a bigger portion of the entrance pupil

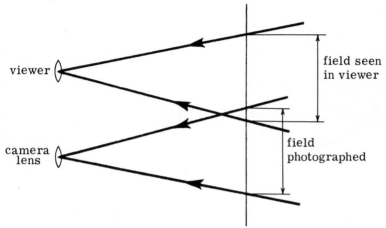

Fig. 13-7.   Parallax between camera image and viewfinder.

of L, but the area CD would decrease.   The source is the field stop
of the system.   One could improve the situation by increasing the
size of the source.   This, however, presents many practical difficulties.   More heat is generated; we would again have to place B
further away, and many bright light sources, such as the carbon
arc, cannot be made larger.   We could insert a diffusing screen
between B and A which would increase the area CD but we would
lose a lot of light.

By using an additional lens system we can arrive at a solution
where the source does not have the role of field stop (Fig. 13-9).
The lens system M, called the condenser, images the source B in

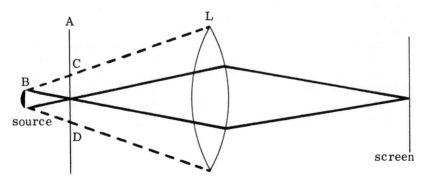

Fig. 13-8.   Illumination in a projector without condenser.

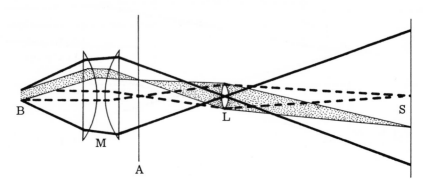

Fig. 13-9.   Illumination in a projector with condenser.

the entrance pupil of the lens L.   By giving M the right power and
choosing the right position of the source, we can have the source
imaged with such a magnification that the entrance pupil of L is
practically filled.   We see that this does not have to be a perfect
image.   If the aberrations are not so large that a portion of the image of the source falls outside the entrance pupil, they do not affect
the final image of A.   Very often a set of two plano-convex lenses
is used as a condenser.   The focal length of the projection lens is
determined by the size of the object, the size of the desired image,
and the distance available between projector and screen.

The objectives used are very often of the Petzval type.   Usually a small field and F number are desired, and this type has just
these optical properties.   Furthermore, the doublet closest to the
film is often uncemented, which is an advantage when the lens gets
hot.   A blower is often incorporated to reduce the temperature
reached by the film during projection.   Heat-absorbing or heat-
reflecting glass can also be used for the same purpose.

The projection of opaque objects presents a completely different problem.   Here only diffuse reflected light from the object
reaches the lens (Fig. 13-10 shows a setup to do this).   It is very
difficult to get enough light in the final image, and the use of
brighter lights is limited because of the enormous amount of heat
created by these sources.

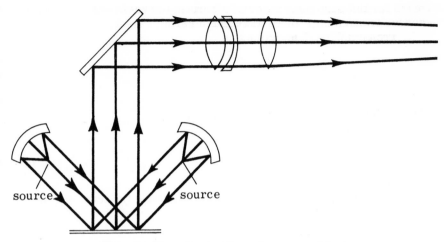

Fig. 13-10.   Projection of opaque objects.

FILTERS

Although there are many different types of filters, we shall describe only a few of the most common types.

a.   Glass and gelatin filters.   These filters absorb light of various wavelengths in different amounts.

The absorption is described with Lambert's law.

$$I = I_0 e^{-kx} \qquad\qquad\qquad (13\text{-}9)$$

where

        I_0 = the intensity of the incoming light
        k = the absorption coefficient
        x = the thickness of the absorbing layer

For an actual filter we also have to take reflection losses into account.   The absorption coefficient is usually determined by measuring I for two samples of the same material, but each of a different thickness.   In this way the reflection losses cancel out in the calculation.

Filter characteristics can be plotted in two ways.   A plot is made for the particular filter of a certain thickness—of wavelength versus transmission or of wavelength versus density.

Transmission T is defined as

$$T = \frac{I}{I_0} \tag{13-10}$$

This ratio is often also given in percentages.

Density D is defined as

$$D = \log \frac{1}{T} \tag{13-11}$$

For completeness we shall describe at this time the term opacity O, which is sometimes used.

$$O = \frac{1}{T} \tag{13-12}$$

Table 13-1 shows the above quantities for various values of T.

In Fig. 13-11 we show the curves for several filters. It must be remembered that practically all materials act as filters. They may have good transmission over the visible region but will absorb at other wavelengths. In Fig. 13-12 we show some other optical materials.

b. Interference filters. This type of filter consists of a spacer layer having a highly reflecting surface on each side. The light leaving the filter consists of many interfering bundles, the first one going directly through, the second going through after reflecting back and forth once in the spacer layer, and the third being reflected back and forth twice, etc. Suppose that the amplitude ratio between the second and first bundles is given by f. The intensity of the light passed by the filter is shown in Fig. 13-13, where e represents the thickness of the spacer layer. For some wavelengths the optical path difference between successive bundles is λ, and these bundles will add in amplitude. For others, the path difference will be $\lambda/2$ and will result in an amplitude of 0. The filter will thus pass some wavelengths while others are not passed. The width of the wavelength region passed is dependent on the quality of the reflecting layers. Usually only one of these bands is transmitted and the others are eliminated by glass filters.

These filters can be made to cover the whole visible region and the near infrared. The bandwidth (the wavelength difference between the two wavelengths where the transmission is 50 per cent of the peak value) can be made in the order of 30 Å in the visible region.

Table 13-1

T	O	D	T	O	D
100	1.00	0.000	49	2.04	0.310
99	1.01	0.004	48	2.08	0.318
98	1.02	0.009	47	2.13	0.328
97	1.03	0.013	46	2.17	0.337
96	1.04	0.017	45	2.22	0.346
95	1.05	0.021	44	2.27	0.356
94	1.06	0.025	43	2.33	0.367
93	1.08	0.033	42	2.28	0.377
92	1.09	0.037	41	2.44	0.386
91	1.10	0.041	40	2.50	0.398
90	1.11	0.045	39	2.56	0.408
89	1.12	0.049	38	2.63	0.420
88	1.14	0.057	37	2.70	0.431
87	1.15	0.061	36	2.78	0.444
86	1.16	0.065	35	2.86	0.456
85	1.18	0.072	34	2.94	0.467
84	1.19	0.076	33	3.03	0.481
83	1.20	0.079	32	3.13	0.496
82	1.22	0.086	31	3.23	0.509
81	1.23	0.090	30	3.33	0.522
80	1.25	0.097	29	3.45	0.538
79	1.27	0.100	28	3.57	0.553
78	1.28	0.107	27	3.70	0.568
77	1.30	0.114	26	3.85	0.586
76	1.32	0.121	25	4.00	0.602
75	1.33	0.124	24	4.17	0.620
74	1.35	0.130	23	4.35	0.639
73	1.37	0.137	22	4.55	0.658
72	1.39	0.143	21	4.76	0.678
71	1.41	0.149	20	5.00	0.70
70	1.43	0.155	19	5.26	0.72
69	1.45	0.161	18	5.56	0.75
68	1.47	0.167	17	5.88	0.77
67	1.49	0.173	16	6.25	0.80
66	1.52	0.182	15	6.67	0.82
65	1.54	0.188	14	7.14	0.85
64	1.56	0.193	13	7.69	0.89
63	1.59	0.201	12	8.33	0.92
62	1.61	0.207	11	9.09	0.96
61	1.64	0.215	10	10.0	1.00
60	1.67	0.223	7.9	12.7	1.10
59	1.69	0.228	6.3	15.9	1.20
58	1.72	0.236	5.0	20.0	1.30
57	1.75	0.243	4.0	25.0	1.40
56	1.79	0.253	2.0	50	1.70
55	1.82	0.260	1.0	100	2.00
54	1.85	0.267	0.50	200	2.30
53	1.89	0.277	0.20	500	2.70
52	1.92	0.283	0.10	1000	3.00
51	1.96	0.292			
50	2.00	0.300			

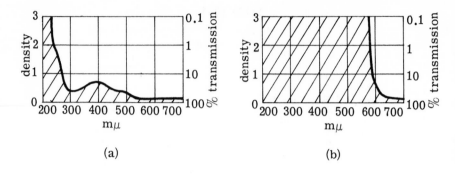

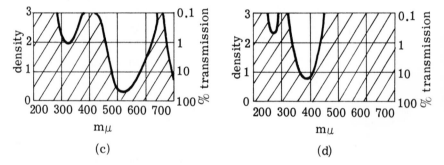

Fig. 13-11. Transmission filters. (a) K-1. (b) Tricolor red. (c) Projection green. (d) Blue-green for microscopy.

For many purposes where we do not require very highly mono-chromatic light these filters are sufficient. They are also very useful for isolating single spectrum lines in a light source emitting more than one line (the mercury green line, etc.).

It is also possible to make interference filters which transmit over a wide wavelength region.

λ, mμ

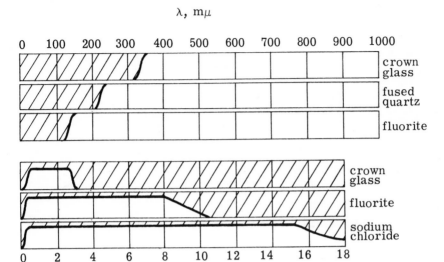

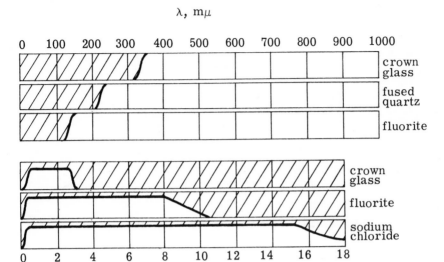

λ, μ

Fig. 13-12. Transmission of some optical materials.

SPECTROSCOPES

The spectrum is formed by means of a prism or a grating. We shall discuss only the prism here.

The deviation δ of a ray passing through a prism (Fig. 13-14) is

$$\delta = <FBC + <FCB$$
$$= i_1 - i_1' + i_2' - i_2 \tag{13-13}$$

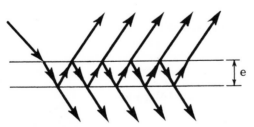

Fig. 13-13. Interference filters.

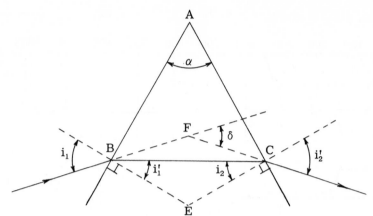

Fig. 13-14. Deviation of a ray passing a prism.

Furthermore, we have the relations

$$i_1' + i_2 = 180 - <\text{BEC} = \alpha \qquad (13\text{-}14)$$

$$\sin i_1 = \mu \sin i_1' \qquad (13\text{-}15)$$

$$\sin i_2' = \mu \sin i_2 \qquad (13\text{-}16)$$

The deviation of the ray goes through a minimum if we change i_1 continuously. From Eqs. (13-13) and (13-14) we determine

$$\delta = i_1 - \alpha + i_2' \qquad (13\text{-}17)$$

and

$$\frac{d\delta}{di_1} = \frac{di_2'}{di_1} + 1$$

This has the value zero for

$$di_2' = -di_1 \qquad (13\text{-}18)$$

Differentiation of Eq. (13-14) yields

$$di_1' = -di_2 \qquad (13\text{-}19)$$

of Eq. (13-15) gives

$$\cos i_1 \, di_1 = \mu \cos i_1' \, di_1' \tag{13-20}$$

of Eq. (13-16) leads to

$$\cos i_2' \, di_2' = \mu \cos i_2 \, di_2 \tag{13-21}$$

From the last two equations we arrive at

$$\frac{\cos i_2' \, di_2'}{\cos i_1 \, di_1} = \frac{\cos i_2 \, di_2}{\cos i_1' \, di_1'}$$

and with the help of Eqs. (13-18) and (13-19) we get

$$\cos i_2' \cos i_1' = \cos i_2 \cos i_1 \tag{13-22}$$

From this, and with the help of Eqs. (13-16), (13-15), and (13-14), we find

$$i_1' = i_2 = \frac{1}{2}\alpha \tag{13-23}$$

Differentiating for the second time shows that this is a minimum. Calling the deviation in the minimum deviation position δ_m we find from Eqs. (13-13), (13-14) and (13-23),

$$\delta_m = 2i_1 - \alpha \tag{13-24}$$

Thus

$$\sin i_1 = \sin \frac{1}{2}(\delta_m + \alpha) = \mu \sin i_1' = \mu \sin \frac{1}{2}\alpha \tag{13-25}$$

or

$$\mu = \frac{\sin \frac{1}{2}(\delta_m + \alpha)}{\sin \frac{1}{2}\alpha} \tag{13-26}$$

This last formula is used to find the refractive index by measuring δ_m and α.

The angular dispersion ζ of a prism is defined as

$$\zeta = \frac{\Delta\delta}{\Delta\lambda} \approx \frac{d\delta}{d\lambda} \tag{13-27}$$

From Eqs. (13-13) and (13-14) we determine

$$\delta = i_1 - \alpha + i_2' \tag{13-28}$$

and thus

$$\zeta = \frac{di_2'}{d\lambda} \tag{13-29}$$

We would like an expression for ζ in terms of $d\mu/d\lambda$. From Eqs. (13-16) and (13-19) we find

$$\begin{aligned}
\cos i_2' \, di_2' &= \sin i_2 \, d\mu + \mu \cos i_2 \, di_2 \\
&= \sin i_2 \, d\mu - \mu \cos i_2 \, di_1' \tag{13-30}
\end{aligned}$$

By differentiating Eq. (13-15) and remembering that i_1 is constant in this case,

$$0 = \sin i_1' \, d\mu + \mu \cos i_1' \, di_1'$$

or

$$di_1' = -\frac{\sin i_1' \, d\mu}{\mu \cos i_1'} \tag{13-31}$$

Using this expression in Eq. (13-30)

$$\begin{aligned}
\cos i_2' \, di_2' &= \sin i_2 \, d\mu + \frac{\cos i_2 \sin i_1'}{\cos i_1'} \, d\mu \\
&= \frac{\sin i_2 \cos i_1' + \cos i_2 \sin i_1'}{\cos i_1'} \, d\mu \\
&= \frac{\sin (i_1' + i_2)}{\cos i_1'} \, d\mu
\end{aligned}$$

and from this, with the help of Eq. (13-14),

$$di_2' = \frac{\sin \alpha}{\cos i_2' \cos i_1'} d\mu \qquad (13\text{-}32)$$

Thus we find for Eq. (13-29)

$$\zeta = \frac{\sin \alpha}{\cos i_2' \cos i_1'} \frac{d\mu}{d\lambda} \qquad (13\text{-}33)$$

The dispersion is a function of i_1 and has again a minimum which does not coincide with the position for minimum deviation. In the minimum deviation position, where most prisms are used (Fig. 13-15), we can rewrite the above formula. We see that

$$t = 2x \sin \tfrac{1}{2}\alpha \qquad (13\text{-}34)$$

$$b = x \cos i_2' \qquad (13\text{-}35)$$

Rewriting Eq. (13-33), using Eqs. (13-34), (13-35), and (13-23), we find

$$\zeta_m = \frac{2 \sin \tfrac{1}{2}\alpha \cos \tfrac{1}{2}\alpha}{\cos i_2' \cos \tfrac{1}{2}\alpha} \frac{d\mu}{d\lambda}$$

$$= \frac{t}{b} \frac{d\mu}{d\lambda} \qquad (13\text{-}36)$$

Even more important than the angular dispersion is the question of

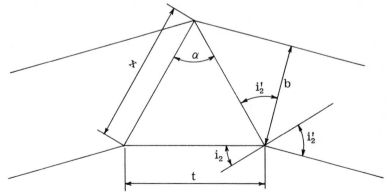

Fig. 13-15. Resolving power of a prism.

how small the wavelength difference between two spectral lines can be, while still being capable of being resolved by the instrument. Taking again the Rayleigh criterion, the angle δ between the two beams with wavelength difference $d\lambda$ should be at least λ/b. Thus

$$d\delta = \frac{\lambda}{b} \qquad\qquad (13\text{-}37)$$

with the help of Eq. (13-27),

$$d\delta = \zeta \ d\lambda = \frac{\lambda}{b}$$

or

$$\frac{\lambda}{d\lambda} = R = \zeta \, b \qquad\qquad (13\text{-}38)$$

where R is the resolving power.

For the minimum deviation position with Eq. (13-35)

$$R_m = t \, \frac{d\mu}{d\lambda}$$

We have to realize, however, that in many instruments this value of R is never achieved because the lenses in the instrument have aberrations, the film used has a grain size too large to image the lines as separate lines, or the slit widths used are too large.

Since the properties of gratings are discussed in most textbooks on physical optics, we shall not discuss them here.

The spectral instruments under consideration consist basically of three parts: (1) the collimator; (2) the dispersion unit (prism, grating); (3) the lens forming the spectrum.

Behind this lens an eyepiece can be mounted for visual examination, an exit slit for isolating very small spectral regions, or a film holder to photograph regions of the spectrum.

The collimator slit in the above derivations is always considered to be infinitely small. In practice, we would have to use finite slit widths to get enough energy through the instrument. As long as the path difference of the light coming from the two edges of the slit is smaller than $1/4\lambda$ (Rayleigh limit), the resolving power of the instrument will remain approximately the same. From Fig. 13-16 we can easily calculate that to the first approximation

$$BC - AC = \frac{bc}{2\ell} \leq 1/4\lambda$$

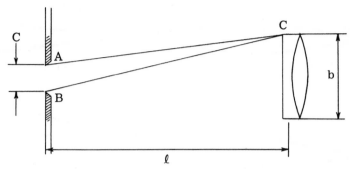

Fig. 13-16.   Influence of slit width.

or

$$c \leq 1/2\frac{\lambda \ell}{b} \qquad\qquad (13\text{-}40)$$

There are two correct ways to illuminate the slit; they are
shown in Fig. 13-17a and c. In Fig. 13-17a, the alignment is very
critical. The proper alignment is done as follows. First, we open
the slit as wide as possible. Then we move the light source until
the light intensity at the collimator is maximum. This is done by
holding a white screen just beyond the collimator lens. Then the
condenser lens is introduced and the source imaged on the slit. It
is advisable to check with the screen to see that the collimator lens
is completely filled with light. This will be possible only when the
condenser lens has a sufficiently large diameter.

Misalignment, as shown in Fig. 13-17b, will not only decrease
resolving power, owing to loss in diameter of the bundle, but also
because of the stray light which will be introduced.

In Fig. 13-17c, the other correct way is shown. Here the condenser is just in front of the slit and the source is imaged on the
collimator lens. The magnification has to be chosen in such a way
that the collimator lens is again completely filled. In this setup
the slit is uniformly illuminated, which is very desirable if one
wants to do photometric measurements of the spectrum.

In most photographic instruments one determines the exact
wavelengths by taking a comparison spectrum on the same plate.
Usually, the iron arc is used to produce this comparison spectrum.
One has to be careful and make sure that the light travels the identical path through the instrument during both exposures because ab-

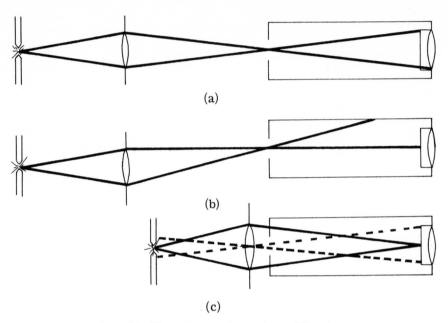

Fig. 13-17. Illumination of a collimator.

errations in the optics might otherwise slightly change the position
of the spectrum lines.

See References 32, 36, 47, 77, and 85 for further information
on this chapter.

Chapter 14

MEASUREMENT, TESTING, AND LINEAR FILTER THEORY

MEASUREMENTS OF THE INDEX OF REFRACTION

a. With the goniometer. The most accurate measurements are made with a goniometer. One way is to measure the minimum deviation. The light source used is monochromatic, emitting the wavelength for which we want to measure the refractive index. Two measurements must be made: (1) the minimum deviation δ_m of the light through the prism and (2) the top angle of the prism α.

With the aid of Eq. (13-24) we can then calculate μ. This formula can be used to find with what precision the measurements must be made. For a precision of 1 in the fifth decimal place the angles must be measured with a precision of 2". This also requires a very high-quality surface on the prism. A prism with a 40-mm face and a radius of 2/3 mile has a difference of 16" in angle if measured on both sides.

An elegant way to measure μ is with an autocollimator as shown in Fig. 14-1. We see that in the autocollimation position

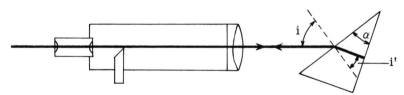

Fig. 14-1. Measuring of the refracting index of a prism.

$$\alpha = i' \qquad\qquad\qquad\qquad (14\text{-}1)$$

and thus

$$\sin i = \mu \sin i' = \mu \sin \alpha$$

and

$$\mu = \frac{\sin i}{\sin \alpha} \qquad\qquad\qquad\qquad (14\text{-}2)$$

We see that it is necessary to measure i and α.

    b. From the critical angle. From Snell's law it follows that, in going from a medium with a lower to a medium of higher refractive index, there is a maximum refracted angle i'_g if i = 90°. Thus

$$\sin i'_g = \frac{\mu}{\mu'} \qquad\qquad\qquad\qquad (14\text{-}3)$$

    Light going from a denser to a less dense medium will be refracted into the less dense medium if i < i'_g. If the angle of incidence is increased beyond this point, total reflection occurs.

    Before discussing the measurement of refraction we will first investigate the behavior of light passing through a plane-parallel plate (Fig. 14-2). Let us assume that

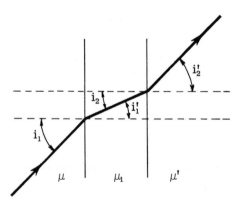

Fig. 14-2. Light passing through a plane-parallel plate.

$$\mu' > \mu$$

Now

$$\mu \sin i_1 = \mu_1 \sin i_1'$$
$$\mu_1 \sin i_2 = \mu' \sin i_2' \tag{14-4}$$

We see that the direction of the light is the same as though the layer with refractive index μ_1 had been omitted. We shall thus also find the same critical angle if $\mu_i > \mu$. If this condition is not fulfilled we shall have total reflection between the media μ and μ_i.

This is important because quite often a thin layer of fluid is used between the sample and the measuring prism in the measurement of the refractive index by means of the critical angle. This fluid layer will not affect the measurements if the layer is plane-parallel or so thin that the angle is within the tolerances. The fluid used has to have a higher index of refraction than the sample.

If we now have light coming from all directions, falling on the interface between the two media with refractive indices μ and μ', we shall have all values of i' up to i_g'. If we now put a telescope in the refracted bundles, we shall have light in all points of the focal plane corresponding to angles smaller than i_g' and no light in points corresponding to angles larger than i_g'. The border between light and dark will correspond to i_g'. See Fig. 14-3, where for each di-

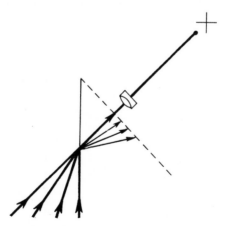

Fig. 14-3.   Critical angle.

rection one ray is drawn.

The way in which the intensity changes in the refracted light can be calculated from Fresnel's formula.

$$a_n = -\frac{\sin(i - i')}{\sin(i + i')} \qquad\qquad (14\text{-}5)$$

$$a_p = \frac{\tan(i - i')}{\tan(i + i')} \qquad\qquad (14\text{-}6)$$

where

a_n = amplitude of reflected light vibrating perpendicular to the plane of incidence

a_p = amplitude of reflected light vibrating in the plane of incidence

The amplitudes of the incoming light are taken as 1. These formulas give the amount of reflected light. We find the amount of refracted light by subtracting the reflected light from the incoming light. If we make these calculations we find that the intensity of the refracted light changes rapidly as it approaches the critical angle. In Fig. 14-4a this is shown for the case where $\mu = 1$ and $\mu' = 1.5$.

It is clear that we can thus measure i_g with good precision. We can also measure by means of the reflected light. We now let the light come from the side where the index of refraction is higher

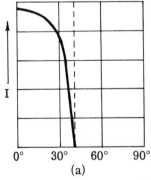

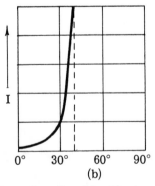

Fig. 14-4.   Light distribution as a function of angle of incidence.

(Fig. 14-4b). We can again calculate the intensity for the reflected light for the same refractive indices as above. Again this is sharp enough to measure i_g'. This way of measuring is helpful if the medium to be measured has a high absorption coefficient. If we use white light the boundary will be colored because of the change of refractive index with wavelength.

The Pulfrich Refractometer

With this instrument we can measure with an accuracy of two units in the fourth decimal place, while we can measure refractive index differences (dispersion) to two units in the fifth decimal place. If we want more precision we must generally use the goniometer. The standard prism P (Fig. 14-5) has two polished surfaces, A and B, which make an angle α with each other. Usually α equals 90°. We measure with refracted light. The ray with grazing incidence along side A will have an angle of refraction equal to i_g', where

$$\sin i_g' = \mu/\mu' \tag{14-7}$$

Using geometrical methods we find that

$$i_g' + i_2 = \alpha \tag{14-8}$$

and

$$\sin i_2' = \mu' \sin i_2 \tag{14-9}$$

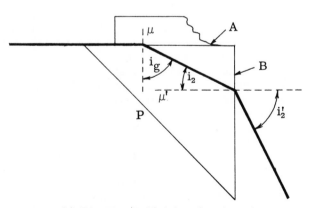

Fig. 14-5.   The Pulfrich refractometer.

From these equations we find

$$\sin i_2' = \mu' \sin(\alpha - i_g')$$
$$= \mu' \{\sin \alpha \cos i_g' - \cos \alpha \sin i_g'\}$$
$$= \mu' \{\sin \alpha \sqrt{1 - \sin^2 i_g'} - \mu/\mu' \cos \alpha\}$$
$$= \sin \alpha \sqrt{\mu'^2 - \mu^2} - \mu \cos \alpha$$

or

$$\sqrt{\mu'^2 - \mu^2} = \mu \cotan \alpha + \frac{\sin i_2'}{\sin \alpha} \qquad (14\text{-}10)$$

From this μ can be calculated if μ' and α are known and i_2' is measured. This is simplified if α equals 90°; then

$$\sqrt{\mu'^2 - \mu^2} = \sin i_2'$$

or

$$\mu = \sqrt{\mu'^2 - \sin^2 i_2'} \qquad (14\text{-}11)$$

The observations are made with a telescope with crosshairs which can be rotated around an axis which lies in surface A and is perpendicular to the paper (Fig. 14-5). It is rotated until the division between light and shadow coincides with the crosshairs and the angular position is read on a scale. The zero position is found by placing the telescope perpendicular to surface B, which can be done because the telescope is actually an autocollimator.

To measure the refractive index of a piece of glass we grind and polish two surfaces on the sample. To ensure angles of incidence equal to 90° there can be no broken edge between the two polished surfaces; the edge has to be sharp.

The sample is then placed on the standard prism with a small amount of liquid between sample and prism. The liquid has to have a higher index of refraction than the sample. Some fluids used are 1-bromonaphthalene ($\mu = 1.65$), methylene iodide ($\mu = 1.75$), and stannic iodide dissolved in methylene iodide.

To measure the dispersion, we use light sources of different wavelengths. The differences in angle between different wavelengths are not measured directly on the main scale, but rather we measure the angular rotation of the telescope, which is done with the help of a micrometer screw which can be read to 6".

Usually each instrument is supplied with three standard

prisms. For the measurement in the region 1.31 and 1.61 a prism with glass 622/359 is used, for the region 1.46 to 1.74 a prism with glass 747/278, and for the region 1.65 to 1.90 a glass 907/217. The last prism has to be handled with extreme care because the glass is extremely soft and easily affected by chemical action.

The Abbe Refractometer

The principal parts are shown in Fig. 14-6. The prism has an angle of approximately 61°. The telescope is fixed with respect to the scale AB. The prism can be rotated around an axis perpendicular to the paper and carries a pointer so the position of the prism can be read on scale AB. Usually the refractive index can be read directly on this scale. Here white light is used to make the measurements. Without taking special precautions we will have a spectrum in the focal plane of the telescope. To make the boundary achromatic a straight-through combination of prisms, which has the opposite dispersion of the combination sample and prism, is used. For each sample-prism combination we need to counteract a different dispersion, and for this reason the combination prisms used can be adjusted to different dispersions.

The prism combination is formed by two identical sets of straight-through prisms (Fig. 14-7). There is no deviation for the d line (Fig. 14-7a) in each set and thus in the combined set. In Fig. 14-7a the two sets counteract each other; in Fig. 14-7b the

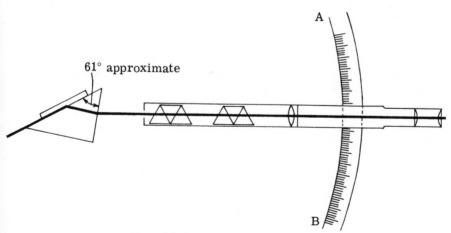

Fig. 14-6. Abbe refractometer.

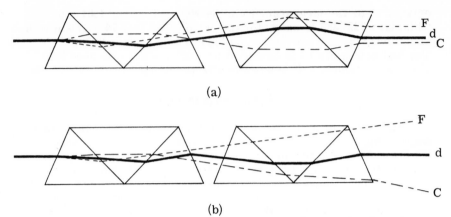

(a)

(b)

Fig. 14-7. Compensating prisms for an Abbe refractometer.

dispersion is maximum. By rotating the two sets an equal amount but in opposite directions, we have the means of adjusting the combination to any desired dispersion between zero and maximum, while the spread of the spectrum always maintains the same direction.

First we adjust the prism sets to counteract the dispersion completely, and then the position of the standard prism is adjusted so that the achromatic boundary falls on the crosshairs. From the standard prism position μ_d is found, while from the position of the dispersion prism sets $\mu_F - \mu_C$ can be found from a table furnished with each instrument.

To calibrate the instrument a standard sample of known refractive index and dispersion is used. If the instrument is off, the direction of the beam inside the instrument can be adjusted.

The measurement of solid samples can again be made in two ways as shown in Fig. 14-8.

If the sample again has two polished surfaces with a sharp edge, the setup as shown in Fig. 14-8a can be used. If only one polished surface is available on the sample, the setup shown in Fig. 14-8b is used. To assure light from all directions the surface AC is ground.

To measure fluids a second prism is provided, one that can be put on the first one in such a way that the space between them is about 0.1 mm. The fluid is introduced into this space. Illumination, as shown in Fig. 14-8c, will never achieve an angle $i_1 = 90°$, but the error in the refractive index measured is smaller than 10^{-4} if the layer is 0.1 mm or less.

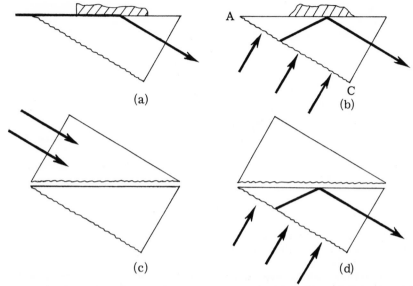

Fig. 14-8. Methods of illuminating the Abbe refractometer.

The standard prism is usually made from heavy flint glass with code 753/276, and the measuring range is from 1.30 to 1.71. The precision is usually 2.10^{-4} for μ_d and 5.10^{-5} for $\mu_F - \mu_C$.

Refractive Index for Fluids According to Pulfrich

We put the fluid V in a cup with a plane-parallel glass bottom (Fig. 14-9), for which the refractive index has to be determined. A telescope with objective B can be rotated around axis A. In front of the objective is a plane-parallel glass plate C which is dipped in the fluid. The position of the telescope can again be read on a scale. The zero point of the scale is determined by autocollimation on the bottom plane-parallel plate.

Spherometers

The mechanical spherometer measures the saggital depth of the surface. To accomplish this a ring is placed on the surface with a feeler in the center. The position of the feeler is measured. Usually the ring is not sharp and care has to be taken that the correct radius is used to calculate the radius of the surface (Fig.

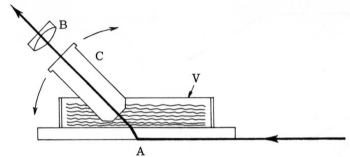

Fig. 14-9. Measuring the refractive index of a fluid according to
           Pulfrich.

14-10). Sometimes other forms of rings are used. This instrument has to be handled with great care in order not to scratch the
optical surfaces.

     Another way of measuring the radii of concave surfaces is des-
cribed below. The disadvantage that only concave surfaces can be
measured is usually not serious because in the fabrication of precision optics test glasses are always available. (Actually very
short convex radii can also be measured.) These are always in a
matching set, concave and convex. This is done to make sure that
the test glasses are spherical. In this case the test glasses will fit
perfectly no matter in what position they are put together. The fit
is judged with Newton interference fringes. The above disadvantage does become serious if we want to measure radii on a finished

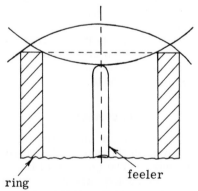

ring

feeler

Fig. 14-10.   Spherometer.

lens without having the test glasses.

The optical principal used is that there are two aplanatic points with magnification $|1|$ for a spherical mirror. One is located in the surface, the other in the center of curvature.

If we take a microscope with crosshairs and illuminate these in autocollimation, we can find these two positions of the microscope with respect to the mirror where the crosshair is imaged on itself, as shown in Fig. 14-11a and b.

By measuring the distance r over which we have to move the microscope we find directly the radius of the surface. There are, however, mechanical difficulties in the precision measurement of this distance. If the microscope is not translated without rotation we can easily introduce an error in the measurement of r. Notice, however, that we do not have to touch the surface at all and thus avoid all possibilities of scratching the optical surface during the measurement.

Another way of using this instrument is shown in Fig. 14-11a and c. In the second measurement, c, a measuring rod is insert-

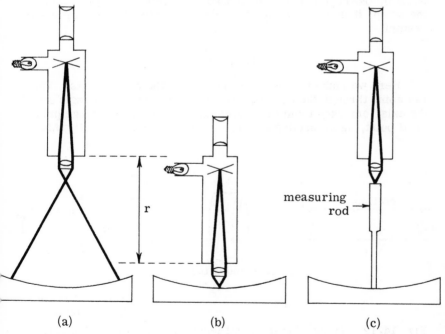

(a)   (b)   (c)

Fig. 14-11. Spherometer with autocollimating microscope.

ed. One end is finished as a small mirror. The rod usually consists of two pieces: one an adjustable piece carrying the mirror,
the other an extension rod of known length.

Measurement of Focal Length

A collimator in which is incorporated a scale with a known distance between its divisions and an objective of a known focal length
gives us an instrument which can be used to find the focal length of
a lens. In addition, we need a small microscope which is mounted
in such a way that it can be moved sideways and this movement
measured (Fig. 14-12).

With this setup we can measure the distance b between the
lines in the image of the scale. If the scale has divisions a distance a apart and the focal length of the objective of the collimator
is f_c, we find the focal length of the lens from

$$f = \frac{f_c}{a}\,b \qquad\qquad (14\text{-}12)$$

If the microscope can also be moved measurably along the axis of
the setup, it is also possible to find the back focal length ℓ_F' of the
system.

Nodal Slide

Here we make use of the properties of the nodal points. The
ray going through the object principal point, making an angle α with
the axis, emerges from the system going through the image principal point, again making an angle α with the axis. Usually this

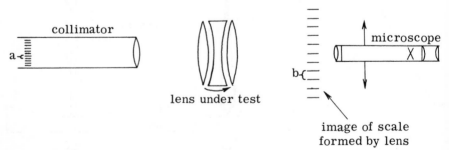

Fig. 14-12.   Measuring the focal length of a system with a cali-
brated collimator.

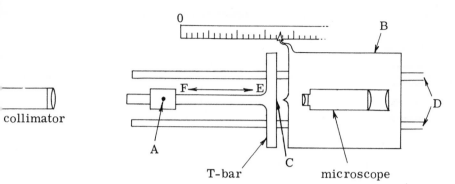

Fig. 14-13. The nodal-slide bench.

method is used for lenses designed for a magnification $\beta' = 0$. We will restrict our discussion to this case. The setup is shown in Fig. 14-13.

The lens can be rotated around point A. The lens mount and T-bar can be shifted together in the direction shown by the arrow. A slide B, on which the microscope is mounted, can be translated back and forth on ways D and is held in contact with the T-bar at point C. The T-bar can be adjusted (the distance FE) with respect to the lensholder. The purpose of the T-bar is to keep the microscope at the right distance from the lens when the combination lens and T-bar are rotated around point A. (The paraxial image plane is perpendicular to the axis of the lens.) First we focus the microscope on the image of the slit (or target) by adjusting the T-bar length EF. Then the lens—T-bar assembly is rotated around point A while watching the image. In general, the image will move sideways. Now the lens—T-bar assembly is moved back and forth with respect to A (note that the microscope moves along with this movement and stays in focus) until the image is stationary while the lens is rotated (Fig. 14-14). Then the position of the microscope is read on the scale which is stationary with respect to A. The pointer on the microscope slide is in the focal plane of the microscope, as is point C. This gives us the focal length directly.

Lensometer

It is often sufficient to know ℓ'_F. This can be measured quickly on a lensometer, which is extensively used by opticians because eyeglasses are thin and $\ell'_F \approx f'$. The apparatus consists of a collimator with objective L_1 and scale G (Fig. 14-15). The scale can be

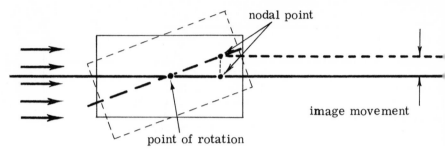

Fig. 14-14. Image movement through a rotating lens.

moved along the axis of L_1. In F'_1 is a pin so placed that the lens to
be measured can be put against it. Behind this is a telescope M,
with crosshairs K, focused at infinity. The target G can be moved
and has a scale such that the 0 on the scale corresponds with the
position G in the focal point of L_1. After the lens is inserted we
move G until we again see the scale sharply in the telescope. If
the image in the telescope is sharp, the image of G formed by L_1 is
in the focal plane of the lens under test. It is convenient to measure image distances in this case, not from the unit points but
from the focal points. Calling these distances g and g' we have

$$g = s - f = s + 1/a$$
$$g' = s' - f' = s' - 1/a$$

Thus

$$gg' = (s + 1/a)(s' - 1/a)$$
$$= ss' - \frac{s}{a} + \frac{s'}{a'} - \frac{1}{a^2}$$
$$= \frac{ss'}{a}\{a + 1/s - 1/s'\} - 1/a^2$$

According to the image relationship [Eq. (4-7)] we have

$$gg' = -\frac{1}{a^2} = -f'^2$$

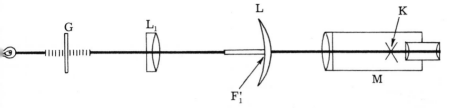

Fig. 14-15. The lensometer.

Now in our setup we have

$$g' = \ell_F$$

Therefore

$$g = \frac{f'^2}{g'} = \frac{f'^2}{\ell_F} = Ca_{vertex} \qquad \text{where } a_{vertex} = \frac{1}{\ell_F}$$

This shows that the scale can be linear in $1/\ell_F$. Usually this scale is in diopters. Here ℓ_F is measured in meters and $1/\ell_F$ is then directly in diopters.

Twyman-Green Interferometer

We have seen that the aberrations of an optical system are caused by deviations of the wavefront from a spherical shape. To measure these deformations an interferometer is used. The schematic of the Twyman-Green interferometer is shown in Fig. 14-16. The converging rays coming from the lens are reflected back with the help of a small spherical mirror with its center of curvature in the image formed by the lens. This arrangement shows double the amount of aberrations of the lens. The resulting interference patterns caused by third-order aberrations are discussed in Chapter 8. A disadvantage of this instrument is that it is difficult to adjust properly. Many other forms of interferometers have been proposed.

Foucault Test

This test is also called the knife-edge test. The setup is shown in Fig. 14-17 (also see Fig. 12-18). If the lens is perfect,

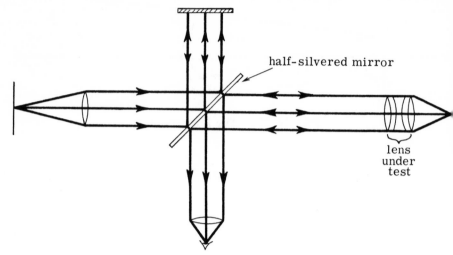

Fig. 14-16.   The Twyman-Green interferometer.

the so-called "cutoff," when the knife edge is brought in, darkens the entire exit pupil of the lens uniformly. Any wavefront aberrations will show up as lighter or darker areas in the exit pupil as the knife edge is brought in. This test is often used to test concave optical surfaces. Here the collimator can be omitted (as shown in Fig. 14-18) by putting the slit in the center of curvature. The light areas are caused by "lightrays," which have aberrations so as to let them miss the knife edge and vice versa.

For a better explanation for all the effects, the wave theory of light has to be taken into account and will be omitted here.

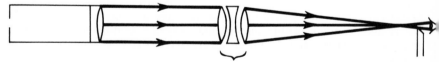

Fig. 14-17.   Foucault test of a lens system.

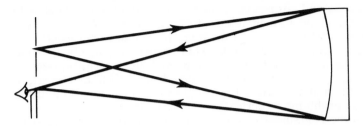

Fig. 14-18. Foucault test for a spherical mirror.

TESTING OF IMAGE-FORMING INSTRUMENTS

There has been, over the years, a number of test charts, differing in their geometry, suggested for testing optical instruments. From points, to lines, to gratings, to annuli and three-bar charts of both high and low contrast, the whole gamut of geometrical shapes has been run. The difficulty of course is that at the very limit where the measurement is most crucial, the images of points, lines, bars, annuli, etc. very often no longer resemble points, lines, bars, annuli, etc. That is, under the mapping, from object to image space that characterize image formation by a lens, these geometric shapes are not invariants. The question arises then whether there exist geometrical patterns which are invariant under this transformation. First we must define the transformation. Restricting ourselves to the objects that are most often encountered in practice, self-luminous or incoherently illuminated objects, we say that the transformation from object to image space is linear. We mean by this that adding two brightness distributions in object space results in adding their image distributions in the image space and that doubling the brightness of an object results in doubling the image brightness. Furthermore, with an approximation that is quite valid over small patches of the image space,* we add the condition that the transformation be translationally invariant; that is, displacing the object structure merely results in a translation, without change of form, of the image structure. It is not difficult to show that the function (eigenfunction) which is invariant under these linear and translational operations has the form of a sinusoid. Moreover, all other geometric structures can be decomposed into a linear sum of sinusoids (Fourier analysis), each component of which can be, conceptually, passed through the system

---

*Regions defined such that we can assume the aberrations within each patch do not change drastically.

separately and later recombined to describe the image structure. In short, using a sinusoidal test chart, the image will always also be sinusoidal with at most the amplitude (contrast reduction) and phase (spatial shift) altered. This reduces the number of quantities to be measured to a minimum, and all the fruitful techniques (with minor changes) that have been developed in electrical, mechanical, and acoustical linear-filter theory can now be brought to bear on problems in optical image formation.

In the remainder of this section we shall confine our attention to one-dimensional variations only. First, for purposes of illustration, we shall discuss the imaging of one-dimensional structures by cylindrical lenses or second, when dealing with spherical lenses, we shall make an appeal to the fact that the general two-dimensional image-evaluation problem can first be decomposed into that of determining what happens to long line structures at a given angle of orientation; later we can combine this information for various azimuth angles.

Suppose now we ignore aberration and diffraction effects and merely ask: "What happens to the image of a long thin line source formed by a cylindrical lens as we move out of focus?" It is quite clear that the "impulse response" or "spread function" for this simplified case is just the rectangular distribution shown in Fig. 14-19. Moreover, we can construct from this the image of an extended object, for example, the bar chart shown in Fig. 14-20 by decomposing the object structure into a set of impulses $o(x) \, dx$, each of which contributes a spread function of the form $\ell(x' - x)$ in the image plane. The final image is then the superposition of all these distributions in the form

$$i(x') = \int_{-\infty}^{\infty} \ell(x' - x) o(x) \, dx \qquad (14-13)$$

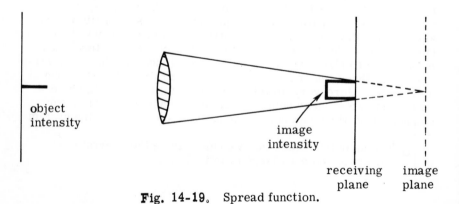

object
intensity

image
intensity

receiving   image
plane   plane

Fig. 14-19. Spread function.

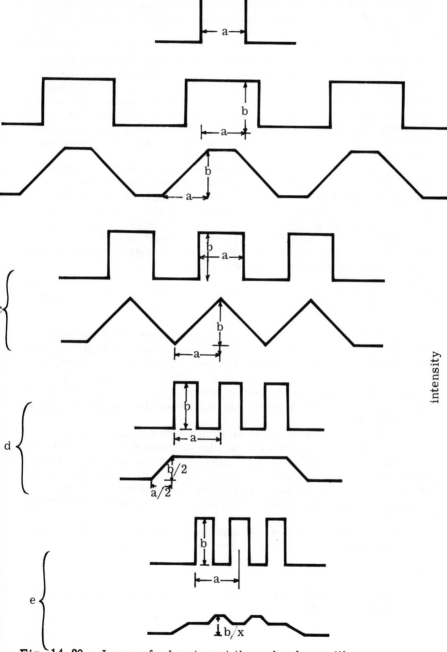

intensity

Fig. 14-20.   Image of a bar target through a lens with a square spread function.

For object structures of relatively simple geometry (for example
that shown in Fig. 14-20b) this convolution can be carried out. As
a matter of fact it is instructive to examine the way in which the
image changes as the detail size begins to approach the dimensions
of the spread function. An observer, confronted with the image
distribution shown at the bottom of Fig. 14-20e might erroneously
conclude that the object consisted of two white bars centered on
points that were actually black. Moreover, he would come to this
conclusion for detail beyond the "resolution limit" (see Fig.
14-20d) of the instrument. This "spurious resolution" is a common pheonomena in image evaluation and is easily incorporated
into the communication theoretic approach.

Continuing to confine our attention to the simple geometry of
Fig. 14-20, we set aside the question of decomposing the object
structure into a set of impulses and now turn to the possibility of
decomposing the object structure into a sum of sinusoids. We can
then ask how the sinusoidal structure of the image is built up. To
determine this we take the Fourier transform* of both sides of Eq.
(14-13) and at the same time invoke the convolution theorem for the
transform of a product. The result is:

$$I(\omega) = \tau(\omega)O(\omega) \qquad\qquad (14-14)$$

where $I(\omega)$ and $O(\omega)$ are the Fourier transforms of $i(x)$ and $o(x)$,
respectively, and where $\tau(\omega)$ (the contrast-transfer function) is the
normalized Fourier transform of $\ell(x)$. For the spread function
shown in the top of Fig. 14-20, $\tau(\omega)$ has the form shown in Fig.
14-21, where the negative region, corresponding to 180° phase
shifts of a sinusoidal pattern, clearly shows the regions of spurious resolution.

Of course many cases arise in practice for which the line
spread function does not have the simple geometry of the rectangular distribution in Fig. 14-21. Very often these point or line images are determined from a measurement on the finished system.
It is useful then to be able to fit several elementary functions to
this measured distribution and from this to determine the contrast
transfer function.

For example, suppose we attempt to approximate the actual
line image by a series of the form

---

*For a periodic structure we would decompose the functions
into Fourier series.

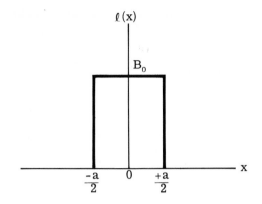

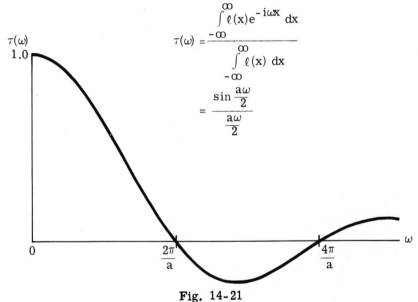

$$\tau(\omega) = \frac{\int\limits_{-\infty}^{\infty} \ell(x) e^{-i\omega x}\, dx}{\int\limits_{-\infty}^{\infty} \ell(x)\, dx}$$

$$= \frac{\sin\dfrac{a\omega}{2}}{\dfrac{a\omega}{2}}$$

Fig. 14-21

$$\ell(x) = \sum_{j=1}^{n} A_j\, f(x, a_j)$$

where a_j are a set of parameters and $f(x, a_j)$ represent some elementary functions. To be more precise, rectangular functions themselves, $\cos^2 (\pi x/2a_j)$ and $\exp[-(x^2/2a_j^2)]$ have been found to

have convenient properties for this purpose. Now making use of
the fact that the Fourier transform of a sum is the sum of the
Fourier transforms, one can deduce directly that

$$\tau(\omega) = K \sum_{j=1}^{n} A_j \, F(\omega, a_j)$$

where $F(\omega, a_j)$ is the Fourier transform of $f(x, a_j)$ and where K is
introduced for normalization purposes. An example of this kind of
useful approximation is shown in Fig. 14-22, where $\ell(x)$ is a typi-

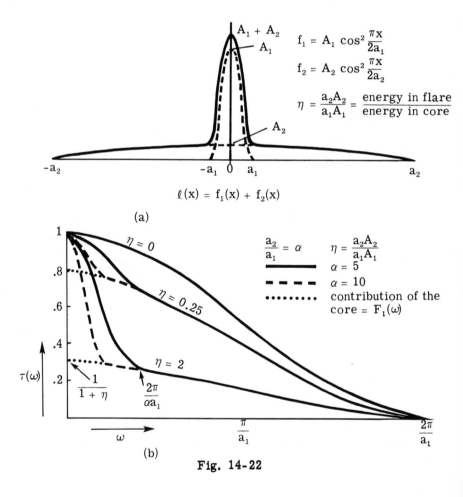

Fig. 14-22

cal white light image exhibiting a hard core with considerable flare light. For this example we take

$$\ell(x) = A_1 \cos^2 \frac{\pi x}{2a_1} + A_2 \cos^2 \frac{\pi x}{2a_2}$$

the first function existing over $-a_1 < x < +a_1$ and the second over $-a_2 < x < +a_2$. The Fourier transforms of these are shown also in Fig. 14-22, together with the sum, to yield the total transfer function. Here the effect of the core and flare light on the image of coarse and fine detail is clearly evident.

Off axis, these point and line images will in general not be symmetric, and it becomes necessary in approximating them to use these basic functions in the form

$$\ell(x) = \sum_{j=1}^{n} A_j \, f(x - x_j, a_j)$$

where both the cosine and sine Fourier transforms are now required to evaluate the transfer function in both amplitude and phase. Fig. 14-23 illustrates the procedure of using two displaced Gaussian functions. The nonlinear phase shift in the frequency response plot resembles the phase shift caused by coma.

Let us now turn our attention to a method of measuring the sine wave response directly. As in electric circuitry where one prefers to record directly the sine wave response (a steady-state signal) rather than the impulse response (a transient signal), so too in optics there are disadvantages in recording accurately the light distributions in a point or line image. Many devices have been proposed and are in use today for measuring the sine wave response. We choose here to describe one* that illustrates the essential features and has the extra advantage of employing an area-modulated sine wave as opposed to a transmission-modulated sine wave test chart.

The basic arrangement is shown in Fig. 14-24. We now wish to calculate the change in intensity as we scan the image-brightness distribution with a fine slit.

For this case we can write

$$o(x, y) = 1 \quad \text{for} \quad -\infty < x < \infty$$
$$o < y < \tfrac{1}{2} + \tfrac{1}{2}\cos \omega_x x$$
$$= 0 \quad \text{everywhere else}$$

---

*Ingelstam, E., Djurle, E. and Sjogren, B., J.O.S.A. <u>46</u> 707 (1955).

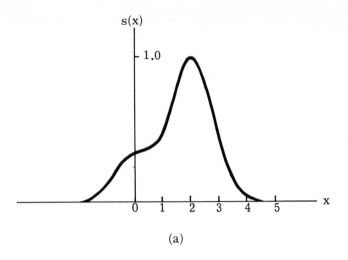

(a)

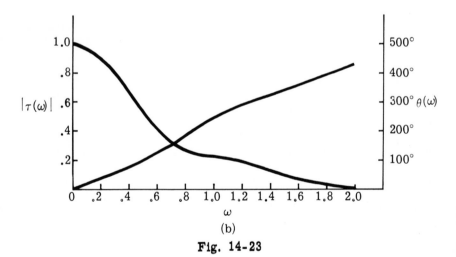

(b)

Fig. 14-23

we then have for the illumination in the image plane

$$i(x') = \int_{-\infty}^{\infty} \ell(x' - x) \, dx \int_{0}^{\frac{1}{2} + \frac{1}{2}\cos \omega_x x} dy$$

$$= \frac{1}{2}\int_{-\infty}^{\infty} \ell(x' - x) \, dx + \frac{1}{2}\int_{-\infty}^{\infty} \ell(x' - x) \cos \omega_x x \, dx$$

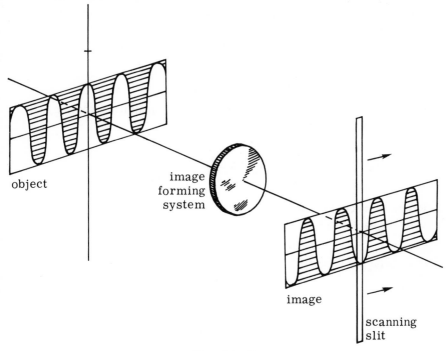

object

image
forming
system

image

scanning
slit

Fig. 14-24

The first integral, representing the total amount of light under the
line spread function, is a constant. Making a slight change of variable to $\mu = x' - x$, we can write the second integral as:

$$\int_{-\infty}^{\infty} \ell(\mu) \cos \omega_x(\mu - x') \, d\mu = \tau_c(\omega_x) \cos \omega_x x' + \tau_s \sin \omega_x x'$$

where $\tau_c(\omega_x)$ and $\tau_s(\omega_x)$ are the real and imaginary parts of the
transfer function defined as:

$$\tau(\omega_x) = \int_{-\infty}^{\infty} \ell(\mu) e^{i\omega_x \mu} \, d\mu$$

$$= \int_{-\infty}^{\infty} \ell(\mu) \cos \omega_x \mu \, d\mu + i \int_{-\infty}^{\infty} \ell(\mu) \sin \omega_x \mu \, d\mu$$

Therefore, by either scanning the stationary image with a slit
(whose own spreading must be taken into account in practice) or by
scanning with the object across the slit, one would record

$$i_+(x') = \frac{c_0}{2} + \frac{\tau_c(\omega)}{2} \cos \omega_x x' + \frac{\tau_s(\omega)}{2} \sin \omega_x x'$$

If on the other hand one were to scan in the opposite direction, we
would record

$$i_-(x') = \frac{c_0}{2} + \frac{\tau_c(\omega)}{2} \cos \omega_x x' - \frac{\tau_s(\omega)}{2} \sin \omega_x x'$$

Hence by recording the maximum and minimum of these readings,
one can determine

$$\tau(\omega_x) = |\tau(\omega_x)| e^{i\theta(\omega_x)}$$

where

$$|\tau(\omega_x)| = \sqrt{\tau_c^2 + \tau_s^2}$$

and

$$\theta(\omega_x) = \tan^{-1} \frac{\tau_s}{\tau_c}$$

One advantage now is that, by Fourier decomposing the object and
multiplying the amplitude at each frequency by the proper factor
and introducing the right phases, the appearance of any image can
be built up. Even when this becomes too complicated, it is, never-
theless, now possible to treat objects in broad categories, depending on their frequency characteristics.
   The greatest advantage, however, lies in the fact that this sine
wave transfer function is often much smoother than the normal
spread function. This is particularly true for lenses which are of
sufficiently good quality that it becomes necessary to describe the
formation of the image by wave-optics methods. In those cases,
for which diffraction effects are important, the sine wave response,
although mathematically equivalent to the light intensity distribution in the point-image diffraction pattern, is a considerably
smoother and hence considerably more convenient function from
which to make an evaluation of the system's performance.

DIFFRACTION THEORY OF IMAGE FORMATION

Turning now to the problem of image evaluation for optical systems of such high quality that we find it necessary to include wave optics effect, we shall find that all the concepts described in the last section can be carried over to physical optics. First, we shall attempt to evaluate the complex light amplitude distribution in the image of a point $a(x', y')$. Second, we shall call upon the fact that in most cases of practical interest the object is either self-luminous or incoherently illuminated,* so that intensities add linearly in the image plane. Therefore we shall define $s(x', y') = |a(x', y')|^2$ as the intensity spread function and take its Fourier transform to determine the transfer function $\tau(\omega_x, \omega_y)$. Finally, since $s(x', y')$ can be written as a product of $a(x', y')$ and $a^*(x', y')$, we shall invoke the convolution theorem for the Fourier transform of a product in order to arrive at an expression for $\tau(\omega_x, \omega_y)$ in terms of the aberration coefficients directly. In this way we will avoid the problems of determining and evaluating the sometimes very complicated point image diffraction structures.

To begin with we say that by a direct application of Huygens Principle the amplitude distribution about a point P' in the receiving plane is a linear superposition of wave disturbances emanating from a surface of constant phase (called the wave front) in the form

$$a(P') = \int\int_{\Sigma} F(A)e^{\frac{2\pi i}{\lambda} W} d\sigma$$

where all constants and obliquity factors have been absorbed into $F(A)$ and where $W = \overline{AP'}$ in Fig. 14-25. In this figure the line AQ represents a ray in the image space.

As elsewhere in this book, the direction of rays in the image space is given in terms of their optical direction cosines (L', M', N'), which are defined as the geometrical direction cosines multiplied with the refractive index of the image space. Now let OS be the normal drawn from the origin in the (x', y') plane onto the ray AQ. Then the optical path length $\overline{PAS}$ considered as a function $E(x, y, L', M')$ of x, y, L' and M' is known as the (point angle) mixed eikonal of the system.[92a] When this function is known, the coordinates (x', y') of the intersection point of a ray with the image plane

---

*For coherently illuminated objects; the complex amplitude adds linearly in the image plane so that $a(x', y')$ itself is the "spread function."

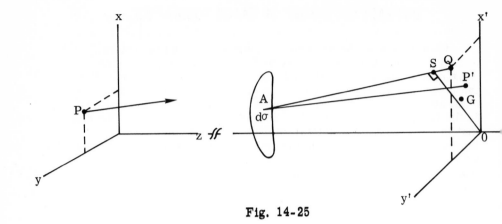

Fig. 14-25

are given by

$$\frac{\partial E}{\partial L'} = -x' \quad ; \quad \frac{\partial E}{\partial M'} = -y'$$

and the direction cosines of the rays in the object space are given by*

$$\frac{\partial E}{\partial x} = -L \quad ; \quad \frac{\partial E}{\partial y} = -M$$

The reason for introducing this mixed eikonal function in place of the wavefront stems from the fact that simple relations exist** between this function and the matrix elements A, B, C and D which emerge as an integral part of lens design. It is, in fact, the existence of these relations that couples the geometrical methods of design to the wave description of the contrast transfer function.

In what follows it will simplify matters considerably if we consider first rays in the meridional plane only. Later the reader can verify for himself that functional dependences on y' are in one-to-

---

*The student of classical mechanics will readily recognize the cannonical formalism of Hamilton that is apparent here.

**Brouwer, W., O'Neill, E. L., and Walther, A., Applied Optics, 2, December (1963).

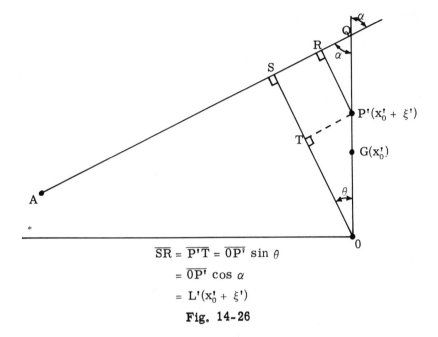

$$\overline{SR} = \overline{P'T} = \overline{OP'} \sin \theta$$
$$= \overline{OP'} \cos \alpha$$
$$= L'(x_0' + \xi')$$

Fig. 14-26

one correspondence with functional dependence on x' for rays out of the plane of the paper.

Turning then to Fig. 14-26, we construct RP' normal to the ray AQ at R. We can then write for the path length $W = \overline{AP'}$

$$\overline{AP'} = E(L', M') - \overline{PA} + \overline{SR} + (\overline{AP'} - \overline{AR})$$

in which we omit the dependence of E on x and y for a fixed object point $P(x, y)$. Moreover $\overline{PA}$ is constant and may be omitted from further consideration.* Finally, since the location of the wavefront is irrelevant, we shall take full advantage of this freedom and remove it to infinity. The effect of this transformation is to reduce $(\overline{AP'} - \overline{AR})$ to zero and to render AP' parallel to the ray AQ.

Before proceeding we remind the reader that AQ is an actual ray in the image space. $\overline{OS}$ and $\overline{P'R}$ are normal projections on to

---

*More precisely, $\overline{PA}$ will not appear in the final form of the intensity distribution since a constant phase factor vanishes in the operation $s = aa^*$.

AQ. P' is the coordinate $(x_0' = \xi')$ in the image plane about which we wish to calculate the diffraction pattern and $G(x_0')$ is conventionally taken as the Gaussian image point or the intersection point of the principal ray with the image plane. Now, from Fig. 14-26,

$$\overline{SR} = \overline{TP'} = \overline{OP'}\sin\theta$$
$$= (x_0' + \xi')\cos\alpha$$
$$= L'(x_0' + \xi')$$

We leave as an exercise for the reader to show that, had we considered a ray out of the meridional plane, we would then end up with

$$\overline{SR} = L'(x_0' + \xi') + M'(y_0' + \eta')$$

so that

$$W = E(L', M') + L'x_0' + M'y_0' + \xi'L' + \eta'M$$

where now a point on the wave front is no longer specified by linear coordinates but rather as a direction. The basic diffraction integral now reduces to

$$a(P') = \int\int_{\Sigma} F(L', M')\exp\left\{\frac{2\pi i}{\lambda}[W_0(L', M') + \xi'L' + \eta'M']\right\} dL'\, dM'$$

where

$$W_0(L', M') = E(L', M') + L'x_0 + M'y_0$$

Introducing the variables* $\nu_x = L'/\lambda$ and $\nu_y = M'/\lambda$, we see that the diffraction integral reduces to a direct Fourier transformation between the linear coordinates in the image plane and angular direction cosines. Moreover, the diffraction integral in this form displays in a transparent way the link between geometrical and wave optics. For, if the aberrations are large, the sine and cosine parts of the complex exponential in the integral will under-

---

*The dimensions of which (length^{-1}) correspond to spatial frequencies.

go rapid oscillations and contribute little to the integral. The major contribution will come from those regions (here directions) for which the phase is stationary. Requiring then stationarity of the exponent with respect to L' and M', we find that

$$\frac{\partial E}{\partial L'} + x'_0 + \xi' = 0$$

$$\frac{\partial E}{\partial M'} + y'_0 + \eta' = 0$$

which are precisely the predictions of geometrical optics.

Let us return now to the diffraction integral and using the new variables ν_x and ν_y we find that we can write

$$a(\xi', \eta') = \int\int_{-\infty}^{\infty} f(\nu_x, \nu_y) \exp[2\pi i(\nu_x \xi' + \nu_y \eta')]\, d\nu_x\, d\nu_y$$

where to emphasize the Fourier transformation we have absorbed all but the linear exponential terms and the finite limits of integration into $f(\nu_x, \nu_y)$. Next we write down the Fourier transform relation between the transfer function $\tau(\nu)$ and the intensity point spread function $s(\xi', \eta') = a(\xi', \eta')a^*(\xi', \eta')$ in the form

$$\tau(\nu'_x, \nu'_y) = \frac{\int\int_{-\infty}^{\infty} a(\xi', \eta')a^*(\xi', \eta')\exp[2\pi i(\nu'_x \xi' + \nu'_y \eta')]\, d\xi'\, d\eta'}{\int\int_{-\infty}^{\infty} |a(\xi', \eta')|^2\, d\xi'\, d\eta'}$$

The denominator being included for normalization purposes. Now, invoking the convolution theorem for the transform of a product, we find

$$\tau(\nu'_x, \nu'_y) = \frac{\int\int_{-\infty}^{\infty} f(\nu_x, \nu_y)f^*(\nu_x - \nu'_x, \nu_y - \nu'_y)\, d\nu_x\, d\nu_y}{\int\int_{-\infty}^{\infty} |f(\nu_x, \nu_y)|^2\, d\nu_x\, d\nu_y}$$

This is a very important result for it allows us to calculate the contrast transfer function directly from the eikonal function [which appears in the exponent of $f(\nu_x, \nu_y)$] and which can be derived from the elements of the geometrical lens design matrices.

In order to illustrate the use of these equations, we would like to adapt them to the case of centered optical systems with circular pupils. To that end we introduce normalized variables

$$\beta_0 = \frac{L'}{L'_m} \qquad \text{and} \qquad \gamma_0 = \frac{M'}{M'_m}$$

where L'_m and M'_m represent the direction cosines of the extreme rays that contribute to the image. For example, on axis, $L'_m = M'_m = n' \sin \theta'$, the numerical aperture of the instrument, while $(\nu_x)_m = (\nu_y)_m = n' \sin \theta'/\lambda$ (see Fig. 14-27). Further in the β_0, γ_0

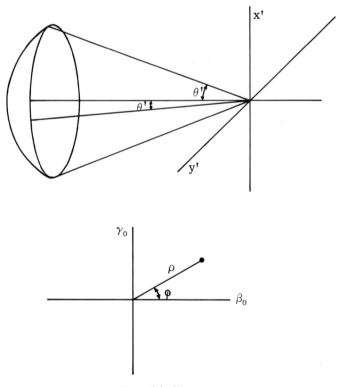

Fig. 14-27

space we define polar coordinates $\beta_0 = \rho \cos \phi$ and $\gamma_0 = \rho \sin \phi$ such that $o < \rho < 1$. With these changes the convolution integral for the contrast transfer function can be cast into the form

$$\tau(s,t) = \frac{\int\limits_{-\infty}^{\infty}\int f(\beta_0, \gamma_0) f^*(\beta_0 - s, \gamma_0 - t) d\beta_0 \, d\gamma_0}{\int\limits_{-\infty}^{\infty}\int |f(\beta_0, \gamma_0)|^2 \, d\beta_0 \, d\gamma_0}$$

where

$$s = \frac{\nu'_x}{\left(\dfrac{n' \sin \theta'}{\lambda}\right)} \quad ; \quad t = \frac{\nu'_y}{\left(\dfrac{n' \sin \theta'}{\lambda}\right)}$$

Let us now calculate the point intensity spread function and transfer function for an ideal lens with uniform amplitude distribution over the pupil and no aberrations. For this case we take

$$f(\nu_x, \nu_y) = A = \text{constant for } - (\nu_x)_m \leq \nu_x \leq (\nu_x)_m$$

$$- (\nu_y)_m \leq \nu_y \leq (\nu_y)_m$$

$$= 0 \qquad \text{elsewhere}$$

Transforming to polar coordinates through the transformation

$$\xi' = r' \cos \epsilon \qquad \nu_x = \nu \cos \phi \, \phi$$

$$\eta' = r' \sin \epsilon \qquad \nu_y = \nu \sin \phi \, \phi$$

we have

$$a(r', \epsilon) = A \int\limits_0^{\nu_m} \int\limits_0^{2\pi} \exp[2\pi i r' \cos(\phi - \epsilon)] \nu \, d\nu \, d\phi$$

From the inherent rotational symmetry in this problem, the result is independent of ϵ and

$$\int\limits_0^{2\pi} \exp(2\pi i \nu r' \cos \phi) \, d\phi = 2\pi J_0(2\pi \nu r')$$

where J_0 is the zero order Bessel function. We then have

$$a(r') = 2\pi A \int_0^{\nu_m} J_0(2\pi\nu r')\nu \, d\nu$$

Now among the interesting properties of the Bessel functions there exists one that says

$$\frac{d}{dx}\left[xJ_1(x)\right] = xJ_0(x)$$

so that

$$\int_0^{\nu_m} J_0(\nu r')\nu \, d\nu = \frac{1}{(r')^2}\int_0^{x_m} J_0(x)x \, dx$$

$$= \frac{1}{(r')^2}\left[xJ_1(x)\right]_0^{x_m}$$

$$= \nu_m^2 \frac{J_1(2\pi\nu_m r')}{(2\pi\nu_m r')}$$

The light amplitude distribution in the point image of an ideal lens is thus given by

$$a(r') = \frac{\nu_m^2}{2}\left[\frac{2J_1(2\pi\nu_m r')}{2\pi\nu_m r'}\right]$$

and the relative intensity in the spread function becomes

$$s(r') = \frac{a(r')}{a(o)} = \left[\frac{2J_1(2\pi\nu_m r')}{2\pi\nu_m r'}\right]^2$$

which is, of course, the celebrated Airy diffraction pattern. Since $J_1(x)$ goes through its first zero at $x = 3.83$, we can determine the radius R' of this diffraction pattern by setting

$$2\pi\nu_m R' = 3.83$$

or

$$R' = \frac{3.83/\pi}{2\nu_m} = \frac{1.22\lambda}{2n' \sin \theta'}$$

Finally, for this ideal case, the convolution integral reduces to the simple geometrical problem (see Fig. 14-28) of determining the common area of two displaced circles as a function of the separation between their centers.

Moreover, because of the rotational symmetry in this case we can for simplicity choose one of the coordinate axes for the direction of shift. From Fig. 14-27 and Fig. 14-28 we see that this normalized integral reduces to

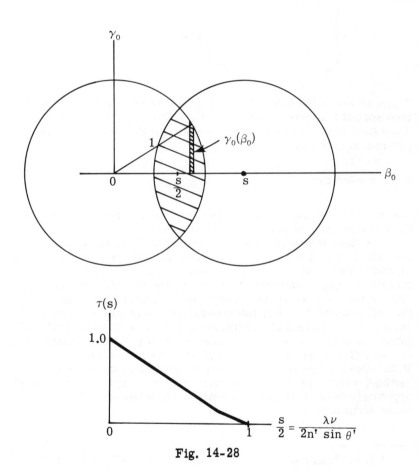

Fig. 14-28

$$\tau(s) = \frac{\frac{4\int\limits_{s/2}^{1} d\beta_0 \int\limits_{0}^{\gamma_0(\beta_0)} d\gamma_0}{\int\limits_{0}^{1}\int\limits_{0}^{2\pi} \rho\, d\rho\, d\phi}$$

$$= \frac{4}{\pi}\int\limits_{s/2}^{1} \sqrt{1 - \beta_0^2}\, d\beta_0$$

or

$$\tau(s) = \begin{cases} \frac{2}{\pi}\left[\cos^{-1}\frac{s}{2} - \frac{s}{2}\sqrt{1 - \left(\frac{s}{2}\right)^2}\right] & 0 \le \frac{s}{2} \le 1 \\ \\ 0 & \frac{s}{2} > 1 \end{cases}$$

A plot of which is shown also in Fig. 14-28 in terms of the normal-ized spatial frequency variable $s/2 = 1/2(\nu)/(\nu_m) = \nu/2(L'_m/\lambda)$. The ultimate ($s = 2$) sine wave resolution limit, therefore, in lines per mm is given by

$$\nu = 2n' \sin \theta'/\lambda$$

where λ is expressed in mm. The sine wave contrast at interme-diate frequencies is given in the Table 14-1.

We close this section by pointing out that, in the general case, the calculation of the contrast transfer function is by no means as straightforward as the ideal case presented here. The interested reader wishing to examine the effect on the transfer function of each of the aberrations taken separately is urged to consult one of the references[59,70,8] For the general and more practical cases in-volving combinations of aberrations, a number of numerical inte-gration schemes have been developed which yield the transfer func-tion at different field angles, focal settings for various colors. H. H. Hopkins,* in particular, has provided an extremely useful method, adaptable even to the more modest computers, and which appears to furnish all the information one might wish for with ade-quate accuracy.

_____

*H. H. Hopkins, Proc. Phys. Soc. B70, 1002, 1162 (1957).

Table 14-1

s	(s)	s	(s)
0	1.000		
0.1	0.936	1.1	0.337
0.2	0.873	1.2	0.285
0.3	0.810	1.3	0.235
0.4	0.747	1.4	0.188
0.5	0.685	1.5	0.144
0.6	0.624	1.6	0.104
0.7	0.564	1.7	0.068
0.8	0.505	1.8	0.037
0.9	0.447	1.9	0.013
1.0	0.391	2.0	0.000

Finally, of course, this is only half the story. If we grant that
a continued monitoring of the transfer function allows one to guide
the progress of a design in a coherent and convenient way, there
still remains the problem of choosing one design over another on
the basis of differing transfer functions. Unfortunately this is a
very complicated question of image evaluation, and to enter into it
here would lead us too far astray. We state simply that, in the
final analysis, whatever criterion is chosen, that choice will include in one form or another weighted averages taken over the
transfer function. The joining of this important function with lens
design methods reflects the extent to which modern image formation optics has succeeded in bringing together wave and geometrical optics in their proper roles.

Appendix A:

INTRODUCTION
TO MATRIX ALGEBRA

Let us assume the following set of equations, representing the transformation of the coordinates x and y into x' and y':

$$x' = ax + by$$
$$y' = cx + dy$$

(A-1)

Let there further be the transformation

$$x'' = ex' + fy'$$
$$y'' = gx' + hy'$$

(A-2)

We can now ask to find the equations describing the transformations of x and y into x'' and y''. This is easily done algebraically by substituting Eq. (A-1) in Eq. (A-2).

$$x'' = e(ax + by) + f(cx + dy)$$
$$= eax + eby + fcx + fdy$$
$$= (ea + fc)x + (eb + fd)y$$
$$y'' = g(ax + by) + h(cx + dy)$$
$$= gax + gby + hcx + hdy$$
$$= (ga + hc)x + (gb + hd)y$$

(A-3)

It is obvious that if there are many of these transformations the work becomes very cumbersome. It is to effect a simplification of these computations that we adopt the system of matrix algebra. Before we can show the simplifications thus introduced we must first briefly describe matrix algebra.

An array of coefficients a_{ij}, set out in m rows and n columns, is known as a matrix of the order m by n or m $\times$ n. The numbers a_{ij} are called elements of the matrix, a_{ij} being the element in the ith row and j^{th} column. The row suffix i ranges over the values 1, 2, ... m, the column suffix j over the values 1, 2, ... n. The matrix as a whole will be denoted by A $[a_{ij}]$ or written out in full array. The element a_{ij} will often be called the $(ij)^{th}$ element of A.

Two matrices A and B are considered to be equal only when they are of the same order m $\times$ n and when all the corresponding elements agree, that is to say when $a_{ij} = b_{ij}$ for all i, j.

We shall at this point consider multiplication of the matrices. The element in the ith row and the jth column of the product matrix BA is obtained by multiplying the elements in the ith row of B into the corresponding elements in the jth column of A and summing the products so obtained. In symbols, if B is of order m $\times$ n and A is of order n $\times$ p, BA = C, where C is of order m $\times$ p and

$$c_{ij} = \sum_{k=1}^{n} b_{ik} a_{kj}$$

It is important to note that multiplication is possible only if the number of columns in B is the same as the number of rows in A.

It is now possible to write Eqs. (A-1) and (A-2) in matrix form

$$\begin{bmatrix} x' \\ y' \end{bmatrix} = \begin{bmatrix} a & b \\ c & d \end{bmatrix} \begin{bmatrix} x \\ y \end{bmatrix} \quad \text{and} \quad \begin{bmatrix} x'' \\ y'' \end{bmatrix} = \begin{bmatrix} e & f \\ g & h \end{bmatrix} \begin{bmatrix} x' \\ y' \end{bmatrix} \qquad (A-4)$$

By substitution we write

$$\begin{bmatrix} x'' \\ y'' \end{bmatrix} = \begin{bmatrix} e & f \\ g & h \end{bmatrix} \begin{bmatrix} a & b \\ c & d \end{bmatrix} \begin{bmatrix} x \\ y \end{bmatrix} \qquad (A-5)$$

Now by matrix multiplication

$$\begin{bmatrix} x'' \\ y'' \end{bmatrix} = \begin{bmatrix} (ea + fc) & (eb + fd) \\ (ga + hc) & (gb + hd) \end{bmatrix} \begin{bmatrix} x \\ y \end{bmatrix}$$

$$= \begin{bmatrix} (ea + fc)x + (eb + fd)y \\ (ga + hc)x + (gb + hd)y \end{bmatrix} \qquad \text{(A-6)}$$

$$x'' = (ea + fc)x + (eb + fd)y$$
$$y'' = (ga + hc)x + (gb + hd)y$$

This is seen to be identical to the result obtained algebraically, (A-3).

Note that in matrix multiplication AB $\neq$ BA.

A square matrix has an appearance similar to that of a determinant, and in this case we can calculate its value as a determinant.

The determinant value of a matrix formed by multiplying a number of matrices is equal to the product of the determinant values of the individual matrices. We shall show this for a matrix of the order 2 × 2 only.

If

$$\begin{bmatrix} A & B \\ C & D \end{bmatrix} = \begin{bmatrix} a & b \\ c & d \end{bmatrix} \begin{bmatrix} e & f \\ g & h \end{bmatrix} \qquad \text{(A-7)}$$

according to our rule the determinant value would be

$$AD - BC = (ad - bc)(eh - fg) \qquad \text{(A-8)}$$

If we multiply the matrices on the right-hand side of Eq. (A-7) we get

$$\begin{bmatrix} A & B \\ C & D \end{bmatrix} = \begin{bmatrix} (ae + bg) & (af + bh) \\ (ce + dg) & (cf + dh) \end{bmatrix} \qquad \text{(A-9)}$$

By working this equation as a determinant we get

$$AD - BC = (ae + bg)(cf + dh)$$
$$- (ce + dg)(af + bh)$$

$$= aecf + aedh + bgcf + bgdh$$
$$- ceaf - cebh - dgaf - dgbh$$

$$= aedh + bgcf - cebh - dgaf$$

$$(ad - bc)(eh - fg) \qquad\qquad (A-10)$$

which equals the value found according to the rule in Eq. (A-8).

PROBLEMS

Solve both by matrices and algebraically.

Example:

$$x' = 3x + 4y \qquad x'' = 2x' + 4y'$$

$$y' = 2x + 5y \qquad y'' = 3x' + 5y'$$

Matrix solution:

$$\begin{bmatrix} x'' \\ y'' \end{bmatrix} = \begin{bmatrix} 2 & 4 \\ 3 & 5 \end{bmatrix} \begin{bmatrix} x' \\ y' \end{bmatrix}$$

$$= \begin{bmatrix} 2 & 4 \\ 3 & 5 \end{bmatrix} \begin{bmatrix} 3 & 4 \\ 2 & 5 \end{bmatrix} \begin{bmatrix} x \\ y \end{bmatrix}$$

$$= \begin{bmatrix} (2 \cdot 3 + 4 \cdot 2) & (2 \cdot 4 + 4 \cdot 5) \\ (3 \cdot 3 + 5 \cdot 2) & (3 \cdot 4 + 5 \cdot 5) \end{bmatrix} \begin{bmatrix} x \\ y \end{bmatrix}$$

$$= \begin{bmatrix} 14 & 28 \\ 19 & 37 \end{bmatrix} \begin{bmatrix} x \\ y \end{bmatrix}$$

Algebraic solution:

$$x'' = 2(3x + 4y) + 4(2x + 5y)$$

$$= 6x + 8y + 8x + 20y$$

$$= 14x + 28y$$

$$y'' = 3(3x + 4y) + 5(2x + 5y)$$

$$= 9x + 12y + 10x + 25y$$

$$= 19x + 37y$$

Problems:

(1) $x' = 2x + 3y$ $\qquad x'' = 5x' + 2y'$

$\qquad y' = 3x + 4y$ $\qquad y'' = 7x' + 13y'$

(2) $x' = 2x + 3y$ $\qquad x'' = 5x' + 2y'$

$\qquad y' = 3x + 4y$ $\qquad y'' = 7x' - 13y'$

(3) $x' = 2y + 3x$ $\qquad x'' = 5x' + 2y'$

$\qquad y' = 3x + 4y$ $\qquad y'' = 7y' - 13x'$

(4) $x' = 5y$ $\qquad\qquad x'' = 5x' + 2y'$

$\qquad y' = 2x + 3y$ $\qquad y'' = 3x'$

Answers:

(1) $\begin{bmatrix} x'' \\ y'' \end{bmatrix} = \begin{bmatrix} 16 & 23 \\ 53 & 73 \end{bmatrix} \begin{bmatrix} x \\ y \end{bmatrix}$

(2) $\begin{bmatrix} x'' \\ y'' \end{bmatrix} = \begin{bmatrix} 16 & 23 \\ -25 & -31 \end{bmatrix} \begin{bmatrix} x \\ y \end{bmatrix}$

(3) $\begin{bmatrix} x'' \\ y'' \end{bmatrix} = \begin{bmatrix} 21 & 18 \\ -18 & 2 \end{bmatrix} \begin{bmatrix} x \\ y \end{bmatrix}$

(4) $\begin{bmatrix} x'' \\ y'' \end{bmatrix} = \begin{bmatrix} 4 & 31 \\ 0 & 15 \end{bmatrix} \begin{bmatrix} x \\ y \end{bmatrix}$

Appendix B:

THE GEOMETRY OF A RAY

To find the direction cosines of the line through the points $Q_1(\chi_1\eta_1\zeta_1)$ and $Q_2(\chi_2\eta_2\zeta_2)$ (Fig. A-1) we construct a line through Q_1 parallel to the χ axis. Q_2S is made perpendicular to this line. We now see that

$$\cos \alpha = \frac{Q_1S}{d}$$

$$= \frac{\chi_2 - \chi_1}{d}$$

Similarly, if β is the angle between Q_1Q_2 and the η axis we find

$$\cos \beta = \frac{\eta_2 - \eta_1}{d}$$

The perpendiculars from Q_1 and Q_2 onto the χ axis are in two planes perpendicular to the χ axis. These two planes also go through the points Q_1 and S. The line Q_1S consequently has the same length as the projection Q_1Q_2 on the χ axis. Thus, it is easily seen that the length of the projection is

$$Q_1S = d \cos \alpha$$

Similarly, the projection on the η axis is given by

$$d \cos \beta$$

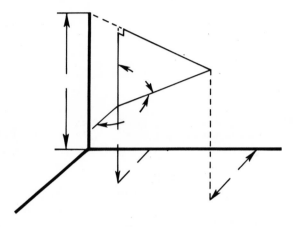

Fig. A-1

REFERENCES

1. E. Abbe, "Gesammelte Abhandlungen," Vol. I (Microscope), Gustav Fisher, Jena, 1904.
2. F. Abeles, "Recherches sur la propagation des ondes électromagnetiques sinusoidales dans les milieux stratifiés. Application aux couches minces," Masson, Paris, 1950.
3. A. Arnulf, La mesure des rayons de courbure des surfaces employées en optique, Rev. Opt., 1930.
4. C. Beck, The Microscope, Theory and Practice (C. Beck, "The Microscope Handbook 1929") R. and J. Beck, London, 1938.
5. A. H. Bennett, "Phase Microscopy Principles and Applications," Wiley, New York, 1951.
6. M. Berek, "Grundlagen der praktischen Optik," W. de Gruyter, Berlin, 1930.
7. H. Boegehold et al., Geometrische Optik; optische Konstante; optische Instrumente," Handbuch der Physik" (H. Geiger and K. Scheel, eds.), Vol. 18, Berlin, 1927.
8. M. Born and E. Wolf, "Principles of Optics," Pergamon, London, 1959.
9. H. Bouasse, "Optique cristalline; double refraction," Delagrave, Paris, 1925.
10. H. Bouasse, "Construction, description et emploi des appareils de mesure et d'observation," Delagrave, Paris, 1921.
11. H. Bouasse, "Optique, géométrique élémentaire; Jacométrie, optométrie," 2nd ed., Delagrave, Paris, 1924.

12. H. Bouasse, "Optique géométrique supérieure; Delagrave, Paris, 1926.
13. G. A. Boutry, "Instrumental Optics," Hilger and Watts, London, 1961.
14. A. Bouwers et al., "Achievements in Optics," Elsevier, Amsterdam, 1946.
15. R. J. Bracey, "The Technique of Optical Instrument Design," The English Univ. Press, London, 1960.
16. W. Brouwer, The Use of Matrix Algebra in Geometrical Optics, Thesis, Delft, 1957.
17. H. A. Buchdahl, "Optical Aberration Coefficients" (G. Cumberlege, ed.), Oxford Univ. Press, New York, 1954.
18. C. Candler, "Modern Interferometers," Hilger and Watts, London, 1951.
19. W. Chauvenet, "A Manual of Spherical and Practical Astronomy," 5th printing, Lippincott, Philadelphia, Pa., 1891.
20. A. E. Conrady, "Applied Optics and Optical Design," Vol. 1, Oxford Univ. Press, New York, 1929.
21. A. E. Conrady, "Applied Optics and Optical Design; part 2," Dover, New York, 1960.
22. S. Czapski and O. Eppenstein, "Grundzüge der Theorie der optischen Instrumente nach Abbe," 3rd ed., J. A. Barth, Leipzig, 1924.
23. A. Danjon and A. Couder, "Lunettes et télescopes, théorie, conditions d'emploi, description réglage," Revue d'Optique, Paris, 1935.
24. C. Deve, "Optical Workshop Principles," 2nd ed., Hilger and Watts, London, 1954.
25. R. W. Ditchburn, "Light," Blackie, London, 1952.
26. P. Drude, "The Theory of Optics," Dover, New York, 1959.
27. W. Ewald, "Die optische Werkstatt," Borntraeger, Berlin, 1930.
28. Ch. Fabry, Les applications des interférences lumineuses, Revue d'Optique, Paris, 1935.
29. "Design of Fire Control Optics," Vols. I and II, U. S. Dept. of Commerce, Office of Technical Services; Washington 25, D. C., 1952.
30. P. Fleury et al., La théorie des images optiques, Revue d'Optique, Paris, 1949.
31. S. Flügge (ed.), "Handbuch der Physik," Vol. 24, Springer, Berlin, 1956.
32. J. Flügge, "Das photographische Objecktiv," Springer, Berlin, 1955.

33. M. Françon et al., "Contraste de phase et contraste par interférences," Revue d'Optique, Paris, 1950.
34. M. Françon, "Le contraste de phase en optique et en microscopie," Revue d'Optique, Paris, 1950.
35. I. C. Gardner, Application of the Algebraic Aberration Equations to Optical Design, Natl. Bur. Std. (U.S.), Sci. Paper No. 550, 1927.
36. R. Glazebrook, "A Dictionary of Applied Physics," Vol. 4, Macmillan, New York, 1923.
37. A. Gleichen, "Lehrbuch der geometrischen Optik," Teubner, Leipzig, 1902.
38. K. J. Habell, "Engineering Optics," Isaac Pitman, London, 1958.
39. W. Merté, R. Richter, and M. von Rohr (eds.), "Hay's Handbuch der wissenschaftlichen und angewandten Photographie. I. Das photographische Objectiv," Vienna, 1932.
40. H. Helmholtz, Handbuch der Physiologischen Optik, 3rd printing, Leipzig, 1909-1911. (English edition, The Optical Society of America, 1924-25.)
41. R. A. Herman, "A Treatise on Geometrical Optics," Cambridge Univ. Press, Cambridge, England, 1900.
42. M. Herzberger, "Strahlenoptik," Springer, Berlin, 1931.
43. M. Herzberger, "Modern Geometrical Optics," Wiley-Interscience, New York, 1958.
44. L. Holland, "Vacuum Deposition of Thin Films," Chapman and Hall, London, 1961.
45. A. G. Ingalls, W. F. A. Ellison, and R. W. Porter, Amateur Telescope Making, 4th ed., Munn, New York, 1945.
46. "International Critical Tables," McGraw-Hill, New York, 1926-1933.
47. D. H. Jacobs, "Fundamentals of Optical Engineering," McGraw-Hill, New York, 1943.
48. E. Jahnke and F. Emde, "Tables of Functions with Formulae and Curves," Dover, New York, 1945.
49. Jenkins and White, "Fundamentals of Optics," 3rd ed., McGraw-Hill, New York, 1957.
50. B. K. Johnson, "Optics and Optical Instruments," Dover, New York, 1960.
51. A. D. König, "Geometrische Optik, Handbuch der Experimental Physik," Vol. XX-2, Akademische Verlagsges., Leipzig, 1929.

52. A. D. König and HorstKöhler, "Die Fernrohre und Entfernungsmesser," 3rd ed., Springer, Berlin, 1959.

53. Z. Kopal, "Astronomical Optics and Related Subjects," North Holland, Amsterdam, 1956.

54. G. Lansraux, Diffraction instrumentale, Revue d'Optique, Paris, 1953.

55. E. H. Linfoot, "Recent Advances in Optics," Clarendon Press, Oxford, England, 1955.

56. R. S. Longhurst, "Geometrical and Physical Optics," Longmans Green, New York, 1957.

57. R. K. Luneberg, "Mathematical Theory of Optics," Brown Univ., Providence, R. I., 1944.

58. A. Maréchal, "Imagerie géométrique aberrations," Revue d'Optique Théorique et Instrumentale, Paris, 1952.

59. A. Maréchal and M. Françon, "Diffraction structure des images," Revue d'Optique Théorique et Instrumentale, Paris, 1960.

60. L. C. Martin, "Technical Optics," Isaac Pitman, London, 1948-1950.

61. L. C. Martin, "Optical Measuring Instruments," Blackie, London, 1924.

62. E. Mascart, "Traité d'Optique," Gauthier-Villars, Paris, 1889-1893.

63. A. A. Michelson, "Studies in Optics," Univ. of Chicago Press, Chicago, Ill., 1927.

64. A. A. Michelson, "Light Waves and Their Uses," Phoenix Science Series, Univ. of Chicago Press, Chicago, Ill., 1902.

65. M. Minnaert, "The Nature of Light and Colour in the Open Air," Dover, New York, 1959.

66. Pol Mollet, "Optics in Metrology," Pergamon, London, 1960.

67. Monk and McCorkle, Optical Instrumentation, Nat. Nuc. Energy Ser., 4, No. 8 (1954).

68. Sir Isaac Newton, "Opticks—Or a Treatise of the Reflections, Refractions, Inflections and Colours of Light," Dover, New York, 1952.

69. B. R. A. Nijboer, "The Diffraction Theory of Aberrations," J. B. Wolters, Groningen, The Netherlands, 1942.

70. E. O'Neill, "Introduction to Statistical Optics," Addison-Wesley, Reading, Mass., 1963.

71. G. Harvey Palmer, "Optics—Experiments and Demonstrations," The Johns Hopkins Press, Baltimore, Md., 1962.

72. R. W. Pohl, "Einführung in die Optik," Frederick Unagar, Berlin, 1940.
73. Precision Measurement and Calibration Optics, Metrology and Radiation, Natl. Bur. Std. (U.S.), Handbook, **77** (1961).
74. Proc. Opt. Convention, London, 1926.
75. Proceedings of the NBS Semi-centennial Symposium on Optical Image Evaluation, Washington, 1951, Natl. Bur. Std. (U.S.), Cir. 526 (1954).
76. Lord Rayleigh, "Theory of Sound," Dover, New York, 1956.
77. Lord Rayleigh, "Scientific Papers," Cambridge Univ. Press, Cambridge, England, 1899-1920.
78. F. Rinne and M. Berek, "Anleitung zu optischen Untersuchungen mit dem Polarisationsmikroskop," E. Schwerzerbart, Stuttgart, 1953.
79. M. von Rohr, "Die Brille als optisches Instrument," 3rd ed., Berlin, 1923. (Part of this is translated by R. Kantlack for the Department of Scientific and Industrial Research, and published by H. M. Stationery Office, London.)
80. M. von Rohr, "Die Binokularen Instrumente," 2nd ed., Springer, Berlin, 1920.
81. Bruno Rossi, "Optics," Addison-Wesley, Reading, Mass., 1957.
82. A. Schuster, "An Introduction of the Theory of Optics," 3rd ed., Edward Arnold, London, 1924.
83. K. Schwarzschild, Untersuchungen zur geometrischen Optik, Abhandl. Ges. Wiss. Göttingen [N. F.] **4**, 1905.
84. G. F. C. Searle, "Experimental Optics," Cambridge Univ. Press, Cambridge, England, 1925. (Half-title: "A Manual for the Laboratory," Cambridge Physical Series.)
85. E. W. H. Selwyn, "Theory of Lenses," Chapman and Hall, London, 1959; Reinhold, New York, 1959.
86. William A. Schurcliff, "Polarized Light," Harvard Univ. Press, Cambridge, Mass., 1962.
87. A. Sommerfeld, "Optics," Academic Press, New York, 1954.
88. J. P. C. Southall, "The Principles and Methods of Geometrical Optics, Macmillan, New York, 1910.
89. J. P. C. Southall, "Introduction to Physiological Optics," Dover, New York, 1961.
90. G. C. Steward, "The Symmetrical Optical System," Cambridge Univ. Press, Cambridge, England, 1928.
91. J. Strong, "Procedures in Experimental Physics," Prentice-Hall, New York, 1939.
92. J. Strong, "Concepts of Classical Optics," W. H. Freeman, San Francisco, 1958.

93. H. D. Taylor, A System of Applied Optics, Macmillan, New York, 1906.

94. S. Tolansky, Multiple-Beam Interferometry of Surfaces and Films, Clarendon Press, Oxford, England, 1948.

95. F. Twyman, "Prism and Lens Making, A Textbook for Optical Glassworkers, 2nd printing, Hilger and Watts, London, 1952.

96. J. Valasek, "Introduction to Theoretical and Experimental Optics," Wiley, New York, 1949.

97. A. Vasicek, "Optics of Thin Films," North Holland, Amsterdam, 1960.

98. E. E. Wahlstrom, "Optical Crystallography," 3rd ed., Wiley, New York, 1951.

99. E. T. Whittaker, "The Theory of Optical Instruments," Cambridge Univ. Press, Cambridge, England, 1907.

100. W. E. Williams, "Applications of Interferometry," Methuen, London, 1930.

101. E. Wolf, "Progress in Optics," Vol. I., North Holland, Amsterdam, 1961.

102. R. W. Wood, "Physical Optics," New York, 2nd printing, 1923; 3rd printing, 1934.

103. J. H. Wredden, The Microscope - Its Theory and Applications, Churchill, London, 1947.

104. Y. LeGrand, "Light, Color, and Vision," Chapman and Hall, 1957.

105. G. Yvon, "Controle des surfaces optiques, qualité des systèmes optiques," Paris, 1926.

INDEX